The Geological Society of America
Memoir 78

MOLLUSCAN FAUNAS
OF THE
FLAGSTAFF FORMATION
OF CENTRAL UTAH

BY

AURÈLE LA ROCQUE

The Ohio State University
Columbus, Ohio

February 29, 1960

Made in the United States of America

TEXT PAGES COMPOSED AND PRINTED BY THE WILLIAM BYRD PRESS
PLATES PRINTED BY THE MERIDEN GRAVURE COMPANY
BOUND BY RUSSELL-RUTTER COMPANY

PUBLISHED BY THE GEOLOGICAL SOCIETY OF AMERICA

ADDRESS ALL COMMUNICATIONS TO
THE GEOLOGICAL SOCIETY OF AMERICA
419 WEST 117 STREET, NEW YORK 27, NEW YORK

The Memoir Series
of
The Geological Society of America
is made possible
through the bequest of
Richard Alexander Fullerton Penrose, Jr.

ACKNOWLEDGMENTS

Thanks are due Dr. E. M. Spieker for suggesting the investigation of the Flag-staff fauna and for conferring with me in the field. I am especially indebted to Mr. James R. Gill for many collections and data on sections. Messrs. S. P. Fagadau, R. E. Hunt, M. S. Johnson, W. N. Gilliland, H. K. Lautenschlager, S. J. Mues-sig, and C. H. Summerson contributed specimens. Dr. George H. Crowl located several fossiliferous localities, which he also helped me sample. During the 1949 field season Messrs. R. H. Crombie, W. C. Hooper, F. R. Kalman, W. C. Prinz, T. H. Riddle, W. W. Shisler, R. K. Smith, D. A. Waldron, and D. C. Wam-baugh, who were then students at the Ohio State University Field Station, actively searched for fossils in the areas they were mapping and located many fossiliferous beds, accurately placed in measured sections. The same enthusiastic co-operation was received during the 1950 season from the Misses M. J. Morrow and P. Smyth and Messrs. R. S. Bowman, D. W. Boyd, B. O. Chalker, D. E. Chase, G. K. Ealy, R. Essig, J. B. Leech, J. W. Reynolds, P. O. Roehl, and E. H. Roseboom. Their co-operation is gratefully acknowledged. The manuscript was critically read by Drs. J. B. Reeside, Jr., L. B. Kellum, F. H. McLearn, and L. S. Russell, whose many valuable suggestions are greatly appreciated.

CONTENTS

ILLUSTRATIONS

PLATES

FIGURES

TABLES

ABSTRACT

The Flagstaff formation of central Utah is divided into three units; the lowest is Paleocene, the middle is Paleocene or Eocene, and the upper is Eocene. The lowest unit contains 28 species of fresh-water and land Mollusca; the middle unit contains 2 species of land snails; the upper unit contains 13 species of fresh-water and land Mollusca. The total molluscan fauna consists of 37 species—5 fresh-water pelecypods, 24 fresh-water gastropods, and 8 land gastropods. Four new species are described: *Elliptio mormonum, Lampsilis spiekeri, Hydrobia ephraimensis, and Carinulorbis utahensis.* The quantitative and volumetric abundance of each species is given. The paleoecology of the lake is examined from the following standpoints: size of the lake, depth of water, chemical composition of the water, fluctuations of the shore line, surrounding land surface, source of sediments, nature of sediments, wave action, evaporation, vegetation, composition and variation of the molluscan fauna. The history of the lake is described from its origin in late Paleocene time to its extinction in Eocene time. In the first phase, the lake was small, with abundant vegetation and a large molluscan fauna. In its second phase, it deepened and expanded considerably; the gypsum content of its waters increased, and the molluscan fauna was wiped out; only land snails and fragments of molluscan shells were preserved. In the third phase, the lake was still large but shallow; a new molluscan fauna invaded the lake and persisted until its extinction. The Flagstaff lake was partly wiped out by encroachment of alluvial-plain sediments and partly merged with the Green River lake which spread into its area from the north.

1

INTRODUCTION

The sequence of Upper Cretaceous and Lower Tertiary nonmarine strata described by Spieker (1946; 1949) in central Utah has proved to be richly fossiliferous. I was privileged to study the faunas of these beds during parts of the summers of 1949 and 1950 and to collect large suites of specimens from them. All the formations from the North Horn (Cretaceous and Paleocene) to the Crazy Hollow (Eocene? or younger) have yielded fossils, some of them in abundance and well preserved. I chose the Flagstaff formation for intensive study because of the abundance and excellent preservation of specimens in many of its beds, the ubiquity of the formation along the Wasatch Plateau and Gunnison Plateau fronts, and the relationship of the Flagstaff with the formations overlying and underlying it.

PURPOSE: The main purpose of this paper is a detailed paleontological study of the Flagstaff formation. The molluscan assemblages in various zones within the Flagstaff are described, and their geographic and geologic distribution plotted. Their stratigraphic value proved to be very real, especially because of the relative abundance of species and forms within particular zones. Interpretation of the succession of molluscan faunas has yielded a detailed history of the Flagstaff lake. This may be of value to geologists in reconstructing the geologic history of the region.

NATURE OF PROBLEM: Interpretation of the Flagstaff molluscan faunas is difficult because constant and widespread stratigraphic planes are not available, either at the base of the formation or at the top. Nor can the origin of the sediments provide a key to the stratigraphic position of a given faunule, for lacustrine beds, dominant in the Flagstaff, are also present in the North Horn, Colton, and Green River formations. Moreover, intertonguing of the four formations is the rule rather than the exception; therefore, the usual bases for the solution of a stratigraphic problem become extremely insecure, and other criteria must be used in addition to the presence or absence of a number of species. Since the environment was lacustrine, it may have been invaded many times by the same species. One must therefore search for minute evolutionary changes that might correspond to the passage of time indicated by the accumulation of sediments. Unfortunately the fresh-water Mollusca are notoriously devoid of rapidly changing external ornamentation. Most of the fresh-water Mollusca bear no more than the faintest growth lines and the simplest of spiral ornamentation. An exception to the rule is the genus *Goniobasis*, which has yielded useful criteria in the details of its profuse ornamentation. Because of these difficulties, the assemblages studied were compared, in addition to the usual methods, from the standpoint of relative abundance of each species within lithologic subdivisions of the formation. Results which appear useful have been obtained by this method. It might be objected that stratigraphic data based on relative abundance of species merely reflect changing environment. This was fully realized in the evaluation of results based on

3

relative abundance, and the data derived from this source have been compared with those yielded by studies of lithology and regional thickening and thinning of recognizable units.

Briefly, the problem was to zone the Flagstaff formation paleontologically by whatever methods might be available, and to check the zones, once they were established, in the type area of the formation, against the stratigraphy and paleontology in other areas. It was soon evident that such an undertaking would involve interpretation of the history of the Flagstaff lake and its influence on the development of the molluscan faunas. Reconstruction of the history of the Flagstaff lake therefore became a secondary purpose of the investigation.

METHODS: Collections were obtained in place, from measured sections. Collections at first were located in the sections unit by unit, but later it became obvious that they were uniform within gross units of the formation, and collections were related thereafter to the base or top of the major unit in which they were found. Large samples were collected wherever possible without emphasis on a particular group, so that as fair a representation of species as possible could be obtained for each unit. Such collecting is necessary if quantitative methods are to be used in the study of a fauna, and the collector must exercise restraint in picking up "float" specimens. In all cases, "float" specimens were kept separate from the collections located in measured sections, and the quantitative data given later in this report are based on unselected samples taken directly from the outcrop.

Work of previous collectors indicated that the Flagstaff formation contained an abundance of relatively small forms. So that a good representation of these minute mollusks could be secured, weathered-shale samples were collected wherever they were uncontaminated by material from overlying beds. This was possible in many shale units of the Flagstaff which alternate with thin limestone beds, for the shale weathers faster than the limestone, and any material collected between limestone ledges is obviously derived from the shale. Several large sacks of weathered material were collected from each outcrop and yielded well-preserved fossils abundant enough to give significant quantitative results.

The usual methods of cleaning, sorting, and identifying were used. In addition, two techniques designed to yield quantitative data are described here so that their value and limitations may be appreciated. In shale samples, in which the matrix could be separated from the fossils, it was soon evident that fossils were more abundant in some units than in others. Measured samples were thoroughly sorted, and the volume of fossils and matrix computed. The percentages obtained are an index of the abundance of fossils in a given unit. Some of them were surprising, for units described in field notes as "coquina, consisting almost entirely of shells" contained only 20 per cent of fossils by actual volume.

The percentage of abundance of the various species represented in one assemblage also proved interesting. The usual terms for expressing abundance ("abundant," "common," and "rare") seemed too inexact to reflect the minute variations encountered in this study. A more sensitive method, used in another quantitative study (La Rocque, 1952, p. 12), seemed to promise better results. Large samples from each collection were sorted, identified, and counted; the proportions of each species were expressed as percentages of the total number of individuals in the collection. From the paleoecologic standpoint, these figures can be deceptive, because they take no account of the volume of the individuals, which varies greatly from one species to another. To restore some degree of balance, the per cent of total volume has been computed for each species in each collection and is given in the faunal lists. It is felt that these methods reflect with some degree of accuracy the variations of the molluscan population of the Flagstaff lake in space and in time. Just how closely they approach accuracy is difficult to estimate, but at least they are better than the empirical measurements implied by such terms as abundant, common, and rare, even with modifiers such as "very" or "less."

STRATIGRAPHY

GENERAL DESCRIPTION OF THE
NONMARINE SEQUENCE IN CENTRAL UTAH

Spieker (1946; 1949) has described the Upper Cretaceous and Lower Tertiary nonmarine sequence in central Utah and the unusual relationships of the formations. From oldest to youngest, they are the North Horn, Flagstaff, Colton, and Green River formations, which consist of rocks compacted from lacustrine and flood-plain sediments varying greatly in thickness from place to place and intertonguing in bewildering fashion. Their description in this report is confined to a minimum sufficient to situate the Flagstaff formation in relation to the North Horn, Colton, and Green River formations and to serve as a background for the paleontologic and paleoecologic discussion of the Flagstaff. The relationship of the four formations is shown in Figure 1.

NORTH HORN FORMATION: This assemblage consists mainly of variegated shales, sandstones, conglomerates, and fresh-water limestones. The formation ranges from 500 feet to more than 3,000 feet thick. In places, as at the type locality (North Horn Mountain, Emery County, Utah), lacustrine shales and limestones form an important part of the section and carry an abundant fresh-water fauna of gastropods and pelecypods. The North Horn lakes (or lake) were extensive, judging by the thickness and lateral extent of the shales. Elsewhere, for example in the Gunnison Plateau, the section is a succession of thick sandstones, probably of flood-plain origin, and is almost entirely barren of fossils. From the standpoint of the present investigation, the most important points about the North Horn formation are that its upper beds were accumulating at the same time as the lower beds of the Flagstaff, with which they intertongue in places, and that the environment in which the lacustrine sediments of the North Horn accumulated was closely similar to that of the Flagstaff; the area of deposition was, however, less extensive than that of the Flagstaff formation. In fact, it may well be that in places the lacustrine beds of the North Horn continue without a break into those of the Flagstaff, although no example of this sort of relationship is known to the writer. The lacustrine molluscan faunas of the two formations are closely similar; one is descended directly from the other with very few new elements from other sources.

Spieker (1949, p. 27–28) has shown on paleontologic evidence that the lower part of the North Horn formation is latest Cretaceous and the upper part is Paleocene.

FLAGSTAFF FORMATION: Like the North Horn, the Flagstaff varies in thickness. Extremes given by Spieker (1949, Table, p. 13) are 200 to 1500 feet. Spieker (1949, p. 31) describes it as follows:

"It is characteristically and dominantly freshwater limestone, but the varieties of this rock alone would require extensive description for full account. Locally the limestone is invaded by other kinds of sediment, not only shale and sandstone, but also gypsum, volcanic ash, oil

7

shale and other bituminous and carbonaceous beds, and locally, conglomerate. Three types of limestone are most common: dark gray, charged with fossils; dark gray, massive, relatively unfossiliferous, and cream to light tan limestone that resembles and indeed might be good lithographic stone. Brecciated and other fragmental limestone is also fairly common, and in places algal (pigeon's egg) limestone is abundant. In the southern half of the Wasatch Plateau much of the limestone is silicified, and Indians have used flint from the formation for various artifacts. Chert beds and nodules are common throughout."

The Flagstaff formation is assigned by Spieker (1949, Table, p. 13) to the late Paleocene. La Rocque (1951) suggested that the upper part of the formation may be Eocene; the age of the formation will be discussed at greater length after its fossil content has been described.

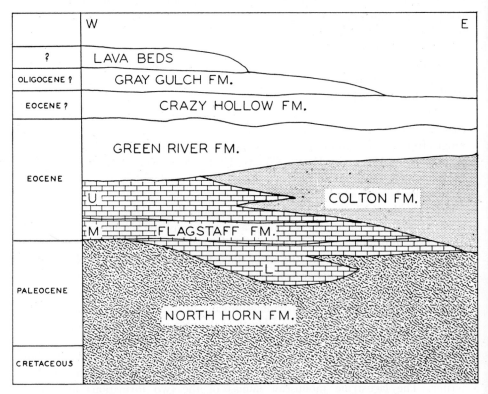

FIGURE 1.—*Stratigraphic relationships of the Flagstaff formation*

After Spieker (1949). The patterns for the formations were chosen arbitrarily and do not indicate lithology.

The Flagstaff intertongues both with the underlying North Horn and the overlying Colton formations. In places, especially in the northern part of the Wasatch Plateau, in the Soldier Summit area, Green River beds immediately overlie the Flagstaff, and we may suppose that lacustrine sedimentation was continuous from Flagstaff into Green River time. Before the implications of these relationships are discussed, a brief summary of the Colton and Green River formations in central Utah must be given.

COLTON FORMATION: Spieker (1949, p. 33–34) describes the Colton formation as

"...dominantly clastic in composition, comprising sandstones and shales of both flood plain and lacustrine origin, but in places the lacustrine zones contain thin beds of limestone. It is normally characterized by bright colors, notably various shades of red, pink, and lavender, and bright bluish-gray. In the type area it is mainly red shale and brown-weathering sandstone, but to the south a wider range of color appears...."

The lacustrine fauna of the Colton is closely similar to that of the upper part of the Flagstaff, from which it is undoubtedly descended, and only a few new elements appear in it; it is likewise closely related to the Green River assemblages but may be distinguished from them by minute differences in the characteristics of the species and the relative abundance of certain forms in the Colton, an abundance which is almost exactly reversed in the Green River formation.

The Colton was provisionally assigned to the early Eocene by Spieker (1949, p. 34). The writer considers this assignment correct and as nearly certain, on the basis of the molluscan faunas, as such determinations can ever be.

GREEN RIVER FORMATION: In the central Utah area the Green River formation is not as thick as it is in the Uinta Basin to the north, but it reaches a thickness of at least 800 feet. Spieker (1949, p. 35) points out the lithologic differences between the Green River formation in central Utah and in the Uinta Basin and western Colorado. For this report, the Green River sequence is important because of its contact with the Flagstaff in part of the area studied. Since it is mainly of lacustrine origin in the area where it immediately overlies the Flagstaff, it is not surprising to find that there is a close relationship between the molluscan faunas of the two formations. These relationships will be detailed in the paleontologic section of this report. (*See* Sears and Bradley, 1925, for further data.)

POST-GREEN RIVER FORMATIONS: In central Utah, the Green River formation is overlain in places by the Crazy Hollow formation (Eocene? or younger), the Gray Gulch pyroclastic rocks (Oligocene?), and mid-Tertiary lava beds. These strata are noted merely to complete the Tertiary stratigraphic section.

FLAGSTAFF FORMATION

DEFINITION AND NATURE: The Flagstaff formation (originally called the Flagstaff limestone) was named and defined by Spieker and Reeside (1925, p. 448-449). The type section is in the slopes of Flagstaff Peak, T. 20 S., R. 5 E., Sanpete County, Utah. At the type locality and in the exposures of the southern Wasatch Plateau, the formation consists dominantly of lacustrine limestones and limy shales with minor amounts of sandstone, gypsum, and other sedimentary rocks. Some idea of the variation in lithology may be gained from Spieker's description (1949, p. 13), already quoted. The vertical and lateral variations within the formation will be discussed later in this paper.

DISTRIBUTION: Figure 2 is a generalized map of the outcrops of the Flagstaff formation. The inferred boundary of Flagstaff outcrops to the north, northeast, and east of the Wasatch Plateau is also shown on this figure; the outcrop areas (also generalized) of the Wasatch beds of Gregory (1950) and Gregory and

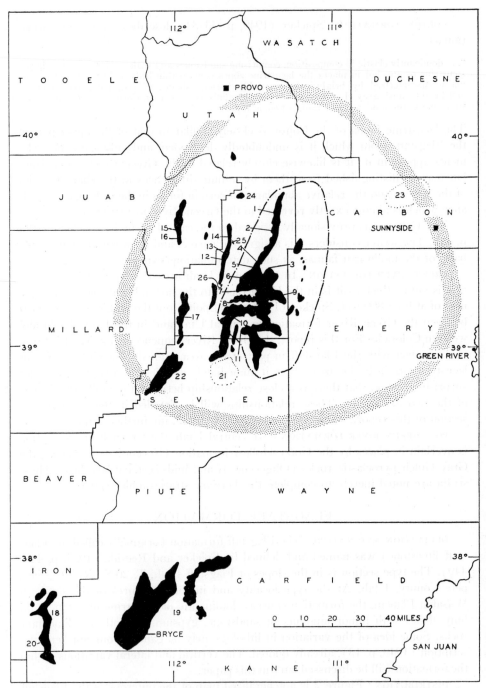

FIGURE 2.—*Map of the central part of Utah showing outcrops of the Flagstaff formation (1–17) and related formations (18, 19)*

The broken line enclosing 1–11 shows the approximate area of the early Flagstaff lake. The stippled boundary is that of the late Flagstaff lake. The unnamed county in the central

Moore (1931), which may be stratigraphically equivalent, at least in part, to the Flagstaff formation of the type area, are also shown. If the known outcrops alone are assumed to have been once continuous, they outline a body of lacustrine sediments about 42 miles wide and 66 miles long and a total area of about 2800 square miles. If the areas outlined by outcrops of probable Flagstaff age to the north, northeast, and east are added to these, the former extent of Flagstaff sedimentation appears enormously greater, and a maximum area of 7000 square miles may be assigned to it. The southern extent of the Flagstaff formation is unknown, as the formation is covered by lava in the Fish Lake Plateau and interrupted by major gaps south of the northern end of the Pavant Range. If Spieker is correct in thinking that parts of the Bryce Canyon and Cedar Breaks sections may be correlated with the Flagstaff, the basin in which sediments of Flagstaff age were deposited occupied a wide belt in the central part of Utah from the Arizona border to the vicinity of Provo.

VARIATION: Spieker's description of the lithology of the Flagstaff (quoted earlier) gives some idea of the variation, both in thickness and lithology, to be expected in the Flagstaff formation. In the following paragraphs the general aspect of sections in selected areas is summarized from the literature and from the writer's own field notes in order to clarify the stratigraphic position of faunas and the discussion of the geologic history of the Flagstaff Lake. Discussion of variation begins at the type locality of the formation and is then extended northward, westward, and southward to other outcrop areas.

In Flagstaff Peak itself scarcely 200 feet of the formation is exposed, but fortunately the exposures in Ferron Mountain and Sage Flat nearby are more than 500 feet thick. In this composite section, in spite of minor variation in lithology, two separate units can be distinguished on gross lithology and faunal content; a lower unit of thin, dark blue-gray calcareous shales alternating with thin limestones of the same color, and an upper unit of rather massive white limestone with minor amounts of light-colored shales and a few pockets and channel sandstones, much gypsum, and some chert. The two units grade imperceptibly into each other but are distinct enough to be separated. The same two units of the Flagstaff may be traced northward and westward where they are exposed in Trail Ridge, Wagon Road Ridge, and the Horseshoe. Along the west front of the Wasatch Plateau the same two units of the Flagstaff are exposed in Pigeon Hollow,

---

part of the map is Sanpete County. Localities 1–11, Wasatch Plateau: 1, Fairview Canyon, colls. 1–3; 2, Canal Canyon, colls. 4–6; 3, The Horseshoe, colls. 7–12; 4, Pigeon Creek Canyon, colls. 13–14; 5, Ephraim Canyon, colls. 15–29; 6, Willow Creek Canyon, colls. 30–32; 7, Manti Canyon, colls. 33–39, 54; 8, Sixmile Canyon, coll. 40; 9, Wagon Road Ridge, coll. 41; 10, Twelvemile Canyon, colls. 42–45; 11, Musinia Peak, colls. 46–47. Localities 12–14, Gunnison Plateau: 12, Little Salt Creek, coll. 48; 13, mouth of Buck Hollow, coll. 49; 14, north of Bear Canyon, coll. 50. Localities 15 and 16, Long Ridge, Juab County: 15, Spring Valley, coll. 51; 16, Mills Gap, coll. 52. Locality 17, Round Valley, Valley Mountains, coll. 53. Locality 18, Wasatch beds of Gregory (1950); Locality 19, Wasatch beds of Gregory and Moore (1931); Locality 20, Cedar Breaks National Monument; Locality 21, Fish Lake Plateau; Locality 22, Pavant Range; Locality 23, West Tavaputs Plateau; Locality 24, Cedar Hills; Locality 25, North Maple Canyon; Locality 26, Christianburg.

New, Ephraim, Willow, Manti, Sixmile, and Twelvemile canyons. Along the east front and all along the top of the Wasatch Plateau, the white, massive limestone is the topmost bed of the formation exposed. In the canyons of the west front of the plateau, the same unit is recognizable but is overlain by another distinct unit of thin, gray to tan shales and limestones bearing much chert, which in turn is overlain by the Colton formation. The boundary between the two formations is not sharply marked, but in all sections examined along the west front of the Wasatch Plateau, the topmost Flagstaff unit of thin shales and limestones could be discerned. Study of the molluscan faunas of the several sections collected shows that they are characterized by distinct assemblages, which will be described later in this report. Minor local variations, for example at the mouth of Sixmile Canyon need not be discussed here.

North of Spring City the Flagstaff crops out along the top of the Wasatch Plateau as far north as Soldier Summit and beyond. These outcrops are generally similar to those of the central Wasatch Plateau, except that the formation thins perceptibly northward.

SUBDIVISIONS: The Flagstaff formation may be subdivided into three gross units in the vicinity of the type section in the Wasatch Plateau from Twelvemile Creek north to Spring City. The lithologic character and thickness of these units from top to bottom, may be summarized as follows:

Unit	Lithologic character	Thickness (in feet)
3	Gray to tan shales and limestones with much chert...........	140-510
2	White limestone with minor amounts of light-colored shales; channel sandstones, much gypsum, some chert..............	30-110
1	Dark blue-gray calcareous shales and limestones alternating in thin beds, 3 inches to 4 feet thick; some thicker shales........	30-755

Unit 1 along the west front of the Wasatch Plateau is invaded in at least two places, Twelvemile Canyon and Pigeon Hollow, by tongues of the North Horn formation. The significance of these tongues will be discussed later.

South of Twelvemile Canyon, units 1 and 2 are absent, and unit 3 gradually changes from the uniform gray to tan shales characteristic of the area north of that canyon to a section of entirely different character consisting of three subunits distinguishable by the contrasting colors of the outcrop as seen at a distance. These subunits of unit 3 together with their lithologic character ande thicknesses are as follows:

Subunit	Lithologic character	Thickness (in feet)
3	Yellow; arenaceous and argillaceous limestones.............	106
2	Red; arenaceous limestones.............................	107
1	White; clayey limestones bearing concretions and algal nodules..	125

The Flagstaff section in the Gunnison Plateau contrasts with that of the Wasatch Plateau to the east and differs in important respects from that of the Valley Mountains to the west and south. It is thinner (maximum 950 feet) than the section in the Wasatch Plateau (up to 1500 feet). Julius Babisak (1959, unpub. M.S. thesis, Ohio State Univ.) noted that the lower part of the formation had not been deposited near Christianburg. The lowest Flagstaff beds here can be correlated with unit 2 of Twelvemile and Sixmile Canyons in the Wasatch Plateau. The beds exposed at Christianburg can be traced northward and westward, and their equivalence to unit 2 of the Wasatch Plateau is further confirmed where unit 3 appears, containing the same fauna as unit 3 in the Wasatch Plateau. The two units of the Flagstaff in the Gunnison Plateau thicken northward to a maximum of 950 feet on Pigeon Creek (Fig. 1, No. 14) (R. E. Hunt, 1950, unpub. Ph.D. dissertation, Ohio State Univ.) and thin southward to 415 feet in North Maple Canyon (Julius Babisak, 1949, unpub. M.S. thesis, Ohio State Univ.).

The Flagstaff formation in Long Ridge has been studied by S. J. Muessig (1951, unpub. Ph.D. dissertation, Ohio State Univ.). He found lacustrine beds throughout the area but noted that they are much fewer north of the Levan Pass road. North of the Levan Pass road in the Long Ridge, the Flagstaff consists dominantly of boulder conglomerates (with boulders up to 5 and 6 feet in diameter, averaging 1 to 2 feet). It seems safe to assume that the margins of the Flagstaff lake lay in the Long Ridge area during part of Flagstaff time; frequent fluctuations are indicated in the lithology of the sections. The Flagstaff is 170 feet thick at the Levan Pass road, where the top is eroded, and reaches 1200 feet in Muessig's East Sage Valley section. The section cannot be subdivided on the basis of fossils, but in light of the correlation suggested for the Gunnison Plateau, it is probable that only units 2 and 3 of the Flagstaff are represented in Long Ridge. This would confirm Muessig's suggestion, based on geologic relationships, that "the Flagstaff of Long Ridge is upper Paleocene and lowermost Eocene" or possibly "completely Eocene."

The variations of the Flagstaff in the Gunnison quadrangle have been described by Gilliland (1951, p. 26–30), who recognizes four different facies (Northern Valley Mountain, Southern Valley Mountain, Fayette, and Willow Creek) and five units (A, B, C, D. and E) within the formation. On paleontologic grounds, Gilliland's units may be correlated, although with some uncertainty, with those recognized in the central Wasatch Plateau, as follows:

Gilliland	This Report
E D C	unit 3
B	unit 2
A	unit 1

In the central part of the Pavant Range, H. K. Lautenschlager (1952, unpub. Ph.D. dissertation, Ohio State Univ.) mapped an extensive area as Flagstaff and correlated his section with units B, C, and E of Gilliland's section. A fossil collection from the "basal gray limestone" (unit B of Gilliland) permitted tentative correlation with unit 2 of the Wasatch Plateau, with important corollaries for the history of the Flagstaff lake. If this correlation is correct, about 2700 feet of unit 3 accumulated in the Pavant Range, and this unit is perhaps equivalent in part to the Colton formation of the Valley Mountains and the Gunnison and Wasatch plateaus.

The northern part of the Pavant Range has been studied by L. M. Tucker (1954, unpub. Ph.D. dissertation, Ohio State Univ.), whose area also contains Flagstaff exposures generally similar to those in the central part of the Pavant Range.

Schoff (1951) provides some information on the nature of the Flagstaff formation in the Cedar Hills, in the northern area of outcrop. The formation there may be as much as 750 feet thick. The lithology described by Schoff (1951, p. 631) suggests that unit 1 of the Flagstaff is absent as it is in the Gunnison Plateau.

North of the Cedar Hills, A. A. Baker (*quoted by* Spieker, 1949, p. 31) ". . . found its [the Flagstaff's] apparent limit in the Wasatch Mountains southeast of Provo." Spieker (1949, p. 31) indicates its eastern limit as follows: "Eastward in the West Tavaputs Plateau I have traced it to a vague remnant in the Sunnyside district; it may continue, invading en echelon the upper part of the North Horn formation, as far as Green River."

To summarize, the Flagstaff in the type area can be subdivided on lithologic grounds into three units. These three units contain distinct assemblages of fossils which permit identification of unit 3 in the Gunnison Plateau and Cedar Hills, of all three units of the formation in the Valley Mountains, and of the upper two in the Pavant Range. The peripheral beds of the Flagstaff in the Long Ridge, north of the Cedar Hills, and to the east in the Tavaputs Plateau, are recognizable as Flagstaff but cannot be subdivided with certainty, although they are probably units 2 and 3 rather than unit 1.

SYSTEMATIC PALEONTOLOGY

GENERAL STATEMENT

The most abundant fossils in the Flagstaff formation are fresh-water mollusks and ostracodes, in that order. In certain beds, the Mollusca make up as much as 20 per cent by volume of the beds; in others they are reduced to rare fragments. Similarly, certain beds are crowded with ostracodes to the exclusion of almost everything else, and others contain very few. Land snails form a small proportion of the fauna. In some beds, they are the only fossils present; they occur as scattered individuals or small groups of specimens concentrated in beds otherwise barren of fossils.

Fish remains, too fragmentary for identification, have been found in several beds of the formation. Hope persists that better material will be found, as well-preserved fish remains occur in the Colton formation, not far above the base, and have long been known in the Green River beds. Those found in the Flagstaff are fragmentary or isolated bones, scales, and teeth. Turtle plates are also occasionally collected, but as yet no complete plastra or carapaces have been collected. Charophytes, studied by Peck and Reker (1948), are abundant in some beds. No mammal remains have been recorded for the Flagstaff formation. The fauna of the Flagstaff is lacustrine, with an admixture of land forms. Its over-all character and the changes which it underwent will be discussed later in this paper.

In the description of the species an attempt has been made, where possible, to appraise the amount of change in each species from division to division of the formation. These changes, however small, have their value both in the description of the progress of evolution within each species and in the identification of the three units of the Flagstaff in the field. Together with the changes in the fauna as a whole, they also help in the differentiation of the lower part of the Colton from the upper part of the Flagstaff. Significant changes are particularly noticeable in the genera *Viviparus* and *Goniobasis;* species of other genera are remarkably stable throughout the formation.

Descriptions of genera and subgenera have been given partly because the literature is somewhat scattered and partly to remind the reader of characteristics which are not repeated in the specific descriptions. The specific descriptions are based on Flagstaff specimens; where they differ markedly from the type specimens or from material from other formations, the differences are discussed in the remarks following each specific description.

Localities are referred to by numbers throughout. Full geographic and stratigraphic details are in the Register of Collections. In stating and discussing the relative abundance of species in the collections, I have attempted to be as objective and concise as possible. The locality number is given first, then the number of specimens, the number of specimens expressed as a percentage of the total number of individuals (I), and the percentage of total volume of the collection

15

represented by the specimens of the species under discussion (V). Collections whose numbers are followed by an asterisk are either too small or lack sufficient variety to be considered significant. The distinction between significant and non-significant collections is arbitrary: collections containing less than 100 specimens or less than 4 species were not considered valid samples of the faunas they represent. Other workers may consider that larger samples, with more varied representation of species, are necessary; if so, the information for each collection is available in the Register of Collections. All measurements are given in millimeters. All materials collected in this study have been deposited in the Geological Museum, The Ohio State University, indicated by the abbreviation O.S.U.

Class PELECYPODA
Order EULAMELLIBRANCHIA
Family UNIONIDAE
Subfamily UNIONINAE
Genus **Elliptio** Rafinesque, 1819

Diagnosis. Shell longer than wide, rhomboid or oval, obscurely biangulate behind; beak sculpture consisting of a few strong ridges, which are nearly parallel to the growth lines or slightly double-looped; surface with fine, closely spaced growth lines. Left valve with 2 pseudocardinal and 2 lateral teeth; right valve with 1 pseudocardinal and 1 lateral tooth. *Type: Unio crassidens* Lamarck

Ecology. The living species of the genus show great tolerance of environment. One species, *E. dilatatus* Rafinesque, inhabits creeks, medium and large rivers, and the Great Lakes. It is equally common on gravel, sand, and mud at depths of less than 1 foot to more than 3 feet. *E. complanatus* (Dillwyn) also has a very wide tolerance of environment, except that it avoids large rivers. It ranges from Georgia far to the north in Canada and seems equally at home in small streams and lakes, on mud, sand, or gravel, and at all depths. In large rivers, it is replaced by *E. crassidens* (Lamarck), which has a preference for fast and rather deep water (6 feet or more). In themselves, fossil species of *Elliptio* are poor indicators of ecologic conditions. The habitat of the Flagstaff species falls well within the wide range of conditions to which the genus can adapt. Obviously these species were lake dwellers, and the Flagstaff lake environment was close to optimum for them.

Remarks. In the Recent fauna, the genus is widely distributed in North and Central America. It is distinguished from the other genera of the family Unionidae on the basis of its soft parts, especially the marsupial portion of the gills. Corresponding constant, although minute, differences in the beak sculpture permit assignment of fossil Naiades to the genus. The genus includes 3 fossil subgenera, *Elliptio s. s., Plesielliptio,* and *Protelliptio,* the last two proposed by Russell (1934, p. 2–3), whose work should be consulted for the assignment of fossil Naiades to this and other genera. Russell (1934, p. 2–3) records typical *Elliptio* from the Lower Cretaceous, *Protelliptio* from the Lower Cretaceous, and *Plesielliptio* from the Upper Cretaceous and Paleocene. The Flagstaff formation has two representatives, one each of *Elliptio s. s.* and *Plesielliptio.* The two species are related only in a general way, belonging, as they do, in two different subgenera developed long before the Paleocene and Eocene. It seems preferable to regard them as belonging to two distinct waves of Naiad migration into the lake from regions as yet unknown.

Subgenus **Elliptio** (*s. s.*)

Diagnosis. Distinguished from *Protelliptio* by the absence of posterior dorsal lines and of posterodorsal plications.

Elliptio mormonum La Rocque, sp. nov.
(Pl. 1, figs. 9–12)

Description. Shell of medium size for the genus, compressed, elongate-ovoid, rounded in front and bluntly pointed behind; postumbonal ridge rounded, without radiating lines; umbonal sculpture of 8 subparallel, irregular ridges, gently rounded in front, obtusely pointed behind. Lateral and cardinal teeth as in the genus, massive in adult individuals. Muscle scars and pallial line as in the genus.

Types. Holotype, O.S.U. No. 20876; paratypes, O.S.U. Nos. 20881, 20882, all from the upper part of the Flagstaff, coll. 1

	Length	Height	Thickness
Holotype, No. 20876	30 mm	20	8
Paratype, No. 20881	55	25	..
Paratype, No. 20882	32	20	..

Occurrence. The species is represented by 15 specimens from 2 of 7 collections from the upper part of the Flagstaff. The data for the 2 collections are as follows: coll. 1, 12 specimens, *I*—3.7 per cent, *V*—9.5 per cent; coll. 29, 3 specimens, *I*—1.3 per cent, *V*—2.8 per cent. It is absent from the 5 other collections from the upper part of the Flagstaff. When it occurs with *Lampsilis spiekeri* La Rocque (coll. 1), it is less common than that species.

Remarks. The species is smaller and much less elongate than *Elliptio silberlingi* Russell. The latter characteristic also separates it from the Paleocene and Eocene species of the genus, such as *E. priscus* (Meek and Hayden). Its closest analogue, at least so far as the outline of the shell is concerned, is in the living *E. complanatus* (Dillwyn), common in the rivers and lakes of the St. Lawrence drainage system and the Atlantic slope. It is easily distinguished from *Elliptio mendax* (White) by the absence of the postumbonal ridges characteristic of that species and from *Lampsilis spiekeri* La Rocque by its beak sculpture, which is of wavy, parallel bars and quite different from the double-looped ridges of *L. spiekeri*.

Subgenus Plesielliptio Russell, 1934

Plesielliptio Russell, 1934, Canadian Field-Nat., vol. 48, p. 3

Diagnosis. "Shell of medium size, narrowly to broadly ovoid. Beak sculptured with a few fine, close-set plications, concentric or double-looped, and having two slightly divergent, straight or gently curved lines directed posteroventrally. No posterior radiating ornamentation. Other shell characters as in the typical *Elliptio*." (Russell, 1934, p. 3.) *Type. Unio priscus* Meek and Hayden.

Remarks. The subgenus is distinguished from *Elliptio s. s.* by the 2 curved ridges radiating from the umbo to the posterior margin; it is distinguished from *Protelliptio* Russell by the absence of posterior radiating plications, which in *Protelliptio* take the form of *Lasmigona*-like plications.

Elliptio (Plesielliptio) mendax (White), 1877
(Pl. 1, figs. 1–8)

Unio mendax White, 1877, Hayden Surv., Bull. 3, p. 605, 611
Elliptio mendax Russell, 1934, Canadian Field-Nat., vol. 48, p. 3
Unio mendax Henderson, 1935, Geol. Soc. Am., Spec. Paper 3, p. 90 (extensive bibliog.)

Diagnosis. Shell of medium size, elongate, subelliptical; beaks in anterior third of shell, with 10–15 concentric loops, intersected by two cordlike ridges running from beaks to posterior margin. Posterior margin sloping obliquely downward and backward from dorsal margin, rounded below to meet basal margin.

Types. Hypotypes, O.S.U. Nos. 20874, 20875, 20879, 20880, 20965

	Length	Height	Thickness
Hypotype, No. 20874	34 mm	21	14
Hypotype, No. 20875	31	..	..
Hypotype, No. 20879	39	27	17
Hypotype, No. 20880	59	34	18
Hypotype, No. 20965	39	27	..

Occurrence. Lower part of Flagstaff formation: coll. 3*, 2 specimens, *I*—16.7 per cent, *V*—49.7 per cent; coll. 12, 8 specimens, *I*—6.3 per cent, *V*—20.6 per cent; coll. 13, 55 specimens, *I*—3.5 per cent, *V*—60.5 per cent; coll. 14*, 2 specimens (the only ones in the collection) ; coll. 17, 2 specimens, *I*—0.7 per cent, *V*—68.6 per cent; coll. 20, 12 specimens, *I*—0.7 per cent, *V*—1.3 per cent; coll. 33*, 2 specimens; coll. 35, 1 specimen, *I*—0.6 per cent, *V*—7.2 per cent; coll. 36*, 5 specimens, *I*—8.6 per cent, *V*—72.2 per cent.

The species is found in 9 of 42 collections from the lower part of the Flagstaff. In several collections, it forms a major portion of the faunule by volume, although it is far outstripped by the gastropods, especially *Hydrobia utahensis* White, in number of individuals. It is the only naiad in the lower part of the Flagstaff and certainly the dominant pelecypod. It is always present in greater numbers than the other two, *Sphaerium* cf. *formosum* and *Pisidium* sp.

The species has been recorded from the Eocene of Utah (*see* Henderson, 1935, p. 90 for references), but it can now be stated definitely that it is found only in the lower part of the Flagstaff, thought to be Paleocene, and that it does not occur in the upper part of the Flagstaff, where its place is taken by an *Elliptio* of the typical subgenus and a species of *Lampsilis* described in this paper, both with umbonal sculpture distinct from that of *E. mendax* (White). Quite possibly many of the identifications in the literature are based on species different from *E. mendax* (White).

Remarks. The outline of the shell ranges (Pl. 1, figs. 1–8) from elongate with a strongly pointed posterior portion to suboval with high, thick shells. These differences are interpreted as sexual dimorphism and, in the writer's opinion, do not deserve even varietal recognition.

Subfamily LAMPSILINAE
Genus **Lampsilis** Rafinesque, 1820

Diagnosis. Shell oval to elliptical, with concentric sculpture only; beak sculpture consisting of double-looped, parallel ridges; in some cases the posterior loop is open behind or the sculpture is obsolete; hinge with 1 or 2 pseudocardinal teeth and 1 lateral tooth in right valve, and 2 pseudocardinal and 2 lateral teeth in left valve; female shell strongly dilated in postbasal region. *Type: Unio ovatus* Say

Ecology. The genus has few definite ecologic preferences. Species have been collected in large and small lakes and rivers, in fast and slow water, in shallow and deep water. Some of the living species of the genus are quite hardy as regards temperature, for they have been able to invade the Mackenzie River drainage and thrive there. On the other hand, some of the species are equally at home in the southern reaches of the Mississippi River drainage. In these respects, it is much like *Elliptio,* with which it is associated, and therefore not particularly significant as an ecologic indicator. The genus is absent from the lower part of the Flagstaff and present in the upper part of the Flagstaff. It is impossible to say whether this is due to chance migration or to some unfavorable factor in the early Flagstaff environment. Certainly, species of *Lampsilis* were widespread in the Cretaceous, but it is just possible that they had not yet extended their range to central Utah in Paleocene time.

Remarks. The genus is widely distributed in the present fauna of North and Central America. The distinctive characters of the genus are those of the soft parts. Living species can be identified as members of the genus by a combination of characteristics which include color and texture of the epidermis, beak sculpture, and the general inflation of the shell, as distinct from the localized dilation of the female shell. Russell (1934, p. 3) has placed in *Lampsilis* several fossil species ranging in age from Lower Cretaceous to Upper Cretaceous. As far as could be ascertained, the species here described is the first to be assigned to the genus from the Eocene.

Lampsilis spiekeri La Rocque, sp. nov.
(Pl. 1, figs. 13–18)

Description. Shell small for the genus, moderately thick; ovate, somewhat inflated in region of beaks; anterior end regularly rounded, posterior end rounded and very bluntly pointed; dorsal and ventral margins gently rounded; posterior ridge indistinct, rounded; beaks slightly elevated above hinge line; beak sculpture consisting of 10–12 double-looped bars, distinct anteriorly, somewhat attenuated posteriorly, the last 2 or 3 bars much less strongly double-looped than the first ones; left valve with 2 pseudocardinal and 2 lateral teeth, upper one short and developed only on posterior portion of hinge; right valve with 2 pseudocardinal teeth and 1 lateral tooth; beak cavities very shallow; anterior muscle scars moderately excavated, posterior scars very shallow. Nacre, as preserved, ashen gray; inner layers, where exposed in broken shells, reddish brown, shining.

Types. Holotype, O.S.U. No. 20872; paratypes, O.S.U. Nos. 20873 and 20883, upper part of Flagstaff formation, coll. 1

	Length	*Height*	*Thickness*
Holotype, No. 20872	23 mm	15	8
Paratype, No. 20873	21	14	8
Paratype, No. 20883	39	26	..

Occurrence. The types, together with 23 other specimens, less well preserved, were found in the upper part of the Flagstaff formation of Fairview Canyon, coll. 1; data are as follows: coll. 1, 24 specimens, *I*—7.4 per cent, *V*—19.1 per cent. The species has not been collected elsewhere, but it very probably occurs in the upper part of the Flagstaff at other localities along the west front of the Wasatch Plateau. When these specimens were collected, they were thought to be young specimens of *Elliptio mendax* (White); only when their beak sculpture had been prepared and studied did it become apparent that they belonged to another genus. Had that been realized in the field, more material from the upper part of the Flagstaff at other localities would have been collected, and most likely *L. spiekeri* would have been included in it. With the data available, it seems to occur in only 1 of 7 collections from the upper part of the Flagstaff. This species is more abundant than *Elliptio mormonum,* the only other naiad in the upper part of the Flagstaff, but it is far overshadowed in numbers by the gastropods of these beds, although not in total volume.

Remarks. This species differs from the Lower and Upper Cretaceous species assigned by Russell to the genus *Lampsilis.* It is less elongate than *L. consueta* (Whiteaves) but not as inflated as *L. sandersoni* (Warren); it is less quadrate in outline than *L. farri* (Stanton). Among living species, it resembles some forms of *L. ventricosa* (Barnes) in outline, but it is not as inflated laterally as that species. *L. spiekeri* may be distinguished from *Elliptio mormonum* by its beak sculpture and the greater inflation of its valves. When the beak sculpture is present, the two species can be separated without difficulty, even in crushed specimens, but when it is absent the only usable criterion is the greater height, in proportion to length, of *Lampsilis spiekeri.* Crushed and distorted specimens are useless for determination unless the beak sculpture is preserved.

Family SPHAERIIDAE

Genus **Sphaerium** Scopoli, 1777

Diagnosis. Shell small, thin, almost equilateral, more or less inflated; surface concentrically striate, striae in some cases almost obsolete; teeth small, 1 cardinal and 2 laterals in right valve, 2 cardinals and 1 lateral in left valve. No distinctive beak sculpture. *Type: Tellina cornea* Linn.

Ecology. Some living species of *Sphaerium* are narrowly limited in their environmental preferences. For example, *S. occidentale amphibium* Sterki lives in the shallow water of temporary ponds and is able to survive the drying of such ponds in late summer. Other species show little preference with respect to kind of bottom, depth of water, or nature of stream or lake. The fossil species are of no special value as ecological indicators except to indicate clean, fresh water without undue amounts of chemical or organic pollution.

Remarks. The genus *Sphaerium* is represented in strata as old as Upper Cretaceous. Many fossil species have been described from insufficient or imperfect material, which makes identification difficult and uncertain at best. The genus is represented by at least one species in the Flagstaff formation.

Sphaerium cf. S. formosum (Meek and Hayden), 1856
(Pl. 2, figs. 1, 2)

Cyclas formosa MEEK AND HAYDEN, 1856, Phila. Acad. Nat. Sci., Proc., vol. 8, p. 115, 279
Cyclas fragilis MEEK AND HAYDEN, 1856, Phila. Acad. Nat. Sci., Proc., vol. 8, p. 115, 279
Sphaerium formosum MEEK, 1876, Hayden Surv., Monogr. 9, p. 526, Pl. 43, fig. 4
Sphaerium formosum HENDERSON, 1935, Geol. Soc. Am., Spec. Paper 3, p. 115 (extensive bibliography)
Sphaerium formosum YEN, 1948, U. S. Geol. Surv., Prof. Paper 214-C, p. 44, Pl. 10, fig. 21

Description. "Shell small, rhombic-orbicular, moderately convex; cardinal margin nearly straight, and of medium length; anterior side rounded; posterior side broader than the other, and truncated a little obliquely above, rounding abruptly into the base below; ventral margin semi-ovate, most prominent behind, and rounding up more gradually in the front; beaks obtuse, a little tumid, rising somewhat above the hinge, nearly touching, and located a little in advance of the middle. Surface marked by small, rather distinct, regular, concentric striae. Length 0.17 inch; height 0.14 inch; convexity, 0.08 inch." (Meek, 1876, p. 526.)

Types. Hypotypes, O.S.U. Nos. 20860, 20929

	Length	Height	Thickness
Hypotype, No. 20860	8 mm	7	5
Hypotype, No. 20929	2.6	2	1.6

Occurrence. The species is found in both the lower and upper parts of the Flagstaff, data as follows: lower part of Flagstaff, coll. 13, 4 specimens, *I*—0.3 per cent, *V*—0.2 per cent; coll. 20, 7 specimens, *I*—0.4 per cent, *V*—0.3 per cent; coll. 28*, 4 specimens; coll. 41, 1 specimen, *I*—0.2 per cent, *V*—1.6 per cent. Upper part of Flagstaff, coll. 29, 4 specimens, *I*—1.7 per cent, *V*—0.5 per cent. This species is one of the few found in both the lower and upper parts of the Flagstaff.

Remarks. The relative scarcity of this species in lacustrine sediments suggests that the specimens have been washed into the Flagstaff lake from streams emptying into it. The fact that most specimens have joined, closed valves makes this unlikely. From this it must be concluded that in both lacustrine phases of the Flagstaff, conditions were such as to be barely favorable for the existence of *Sphaerium.* The factors responsible for this are hard to explain, since other indications are that conditions should have been highly favorable for this small clam. The fact remains that in spite of unfavorable conditions, *S.* cf. *S. formosum* was twice able to invade the Flagstaff lake.

The specimens listed for several localities belong in the genus *Sphaerium,* but specific determination is impossible at present. The specimens appear to be uniform in their characteristics, whether they are from the lower or upper parts of the Flagstaff, but may nevertheless belong to two or more species. The material is too poorly preserved for definite specific identification, so that it appears best to refer all of them with some doubt to Meek and Hayden's species, with which they agree in all external characteristics. For more certain reference to the species, it would be desirable to compare the dentition, not shown in our specimens, with the figure given by Yen (1948b, Pl. 10, fig. 21).

Genus Pisidium Pfeiffer, 1821

Diagnosis. Shell small, inequilateral, strongly inflated; surface concentrically striate or almost smooth; teeth small, under beaks, 1 in right and 2 in left valve; laterals lamelliform, 1 in left and 2 in right valve. No distinctive beak sculpture. *Type: Tellina amnica* O. F. Müller

Ecology. Some living species of *Pisidium* are narrowly limited as to environment, others seem to thrive at all depths, in all kinds of streams and lakes, and on all kinds of bottoms. The fossil species are of no special value as ecological indicators save to indicate bodies of fresh water without abnormally large amounts of pollution or chemical contamination.

Pisidium, sp. undet.
(Pl. 2, figs. 3, 4)

Diagnosis. Shell small, transversely elliptical, subovate, very moderately convex; ends rounded, posterior end narrower than anterior; basal margin ovate, cardinal margin nearly straight, rounding gradually toward the anterior and posterior margins; beaks rise slightly above the hinge. Surface marked with fine concentric striae.

Types. Hypotypes, O.S.U. Nos. 20927, 20928

	Length	Height	Thickness
Hypotype, No. 20927	1.6 mm	1.3	1
Hypotype, No. 20928	2	1.6	1

Occurrence. Lower part of Flagstaff, in 8 of 42 collections, as follows: coll. 13, 2 specimens, *I*—0.1 per cent, *V*—0.1 per cent; coll. 16, 4 specimens, *I*—0.3 per cent, *V*—0.5 per cent; coll. 18, 4 specimens, *I*—1.8 per cent, *V*—12.1 per cent; coll. 19*, 1 specimen; coll. 20, 45 specimens, *I*—2.5 per cent, *V*—1.0 per cent; coll. 21*, 8 specimens, *I*—11.8 per cent, *V*—12.2 per cent; coll. 23*, 1 specimen; coll. 24, 1 specimen, *I*—0.1 per cent, *V*—0.6 per cent. The species has been found so far only in the lower part of the Flagstaff and forms only a minor and inconspicuous proportion of the collections, never exceeding 2.5 per cent of the number of individuals in significant collections and a still smaller percentage of the volume of individuals.

Remarks. The specimens are found with closed valves, which indicates that they probably lived where they are found. The remarks concerning suitability of the Flagstaff lake for the support of a large population of *Sphaerium* apply equally to *Pisidium.* An abnormally small number of specimens is found for both species.

It would be hazardous to refer these specimens to a particular species of *Pisidium* in spite of their good preservation. Until the fossil representatives of *Pisidium* have been revised satisfactorily, it seems pointless to do more than give a generic identification and figures which will permit comparison with other material.

Class GASTROPODA
Order CTENOBRANCHIATA
Family VIVIPARIDAE
Genus **Viviparus** Montfort, 1810

Diagnosis. "Shell dextral, spiral, subconoidal; rather thin, smooth, imperforate or slightly umbilicate; light green or olivaceous, unicolored or banded with brown or tinged with purple; whorls convex, aperture entire, subcircular; lip simple, acute; columellar and parietal margin not usually thickened; operculum concentric, inner margin simple, not reflected." (Walker, 1918, p. 24.) *Type: Helix vivipara* Linnaeus

Ecology. Caution must be exercised in making ecological deductions on the basis of fossil Viviparidae. Many of the fossil forms differ considerably from typical living *Viviparus;* this applies particularly to the species of the Flagstaff, which have many characters in common with living *Campeloma,* although they are distinguishable from that genus on the basis of shell characteristics. There is considerable environmental tolerance in living North American species, as shown by the following examples: *Viviparus contectoides* Binney is found in both lakes and rivers on a mud bottom in shallow water (Baker, 1928, p. 37), but it will also live on a sand bottom in protected situations. It has been found in depths ranging from a few inches to nearly 9 feet; *Viviparus subpurpureus* (Say) shows a decided preference for shallow muddy water but can tolerate changes of water level of considerable proportions.

The species of the genus *Campeloma* are even more tolerant with respect to both quiet water (some will thrive in rapidly flowing streams) and to nature of bottom. I have collected them in shallow sandy lakes and in quiet, muddy expanses of rivers, and in water from a few inches to 5 feet in depth. The presence of *Viviparus* in a Flagstaff collection, especially in appreciable numbers, is indicative more of abundant food supply in the form of minute lower plants and decaying animal matter than of anything else. The genus throve in the Flagstaff environment, which is known to be shallow-water lacustrine from the evidence of the sediments and some of the molluscan associates of *Viviparus,* but its requirements were not always met, as shown by its absence from some of the beds in which it apparently should be found but is not. Certainly *Viviparus* in Flagstaff time was a less hardy group of gastropods than *Hydrobia utahensis,* which occurs in most of the fossiliferous beds of the basal part of the formation; it was also less hardy or less well adapted to conditions of late Flagstaff time, for it is not as common in collections as *Goniobasis* and *Physa pleromatis.* The abundance of specimens in certain beds of both basal and upper parts of the Flagstaff indicates that the species could and did at times live in the lacustrine shallow-water environment of the Flagstaff and that there were times during which it became a prominent element of the Flagstaff fauna.

Remarks. The larger, globose fossil operculates of the Cretaceous and Tertiary of North America are usually referred to the genus *Viviparus* rather than to *Campeloma* Rafinesque on rather uncertain grounds. Nevertheless, reference to *Viviparus* is more satisfactory for the shell lacks the thickening of the columella and parietal wall prominent in *Campeloma,* and the general shape of the shell fits *Viviparus* much better than *Campeloma.* Judging by shell characteristics alone, the two genera seem to be closely related, and very probably the *Campeloma* group is descended from some of the North American Cretaceous forms assigned to *Viviparus.* The two species of the genus present in the Flagstaff are almost undoubtedly correctly placed in *Viviparus* because of the aspect of the earlier whorls, which are strongly carinate; those of *Campeloma* are smooth except for axial ornamentation. The genus *Viviparus* survives in the living North American fauna from Alabama and Florida to Michigan for species considered endemic to North America. Endemic species are absent from the Great Basin area and the West Coast drainage, but these regions are suitable as habitats for the genus, as a few Asiatic species, introduced on the West Coast and elsewhere in the United States and Canada, have established thriving colonies on the West Coast and along the Atlantic seaboard. There is no reason to doubt that they could also become established in the Rocky Mountain area and the Mississippi Valley in general, for they can withstand severe winters, as for example at Ottawa, Ontario, Canada. The fact remains that the native species of *Viviparus,* which almost certainly developed in North America from Cretaceous and Lower Tertiary ancestors, have become restricted to the area east of the Mississippi (with a few possible exceptions) and are at present absent from the Rocky Mountain area from New Mexico and Arizona to Alberta, where they were an important element of the fauna during Cretaceous and early Tertiary times.

Viviparus trochiformis (Meek and Hayden), 1856
(Pl. 2, figs. 5–9)

Paludina trochiformis MEEK AND HAYDEN, 1856, Phila. Acad. Nat. Sci., Proc., vol. 8, p. 122, 279
Viviparus trochiformis HENDERSON, 1935, Geol. Soc. Am., Spec. Paper 3, p. 174 (extensive bibliography)
Viviparus trochiformis YEN, 1948, U. S. Geol. Surv., Prof. Paper 214-C, p. 40, Pl. 10, figs. 2, 2a

Diagnosis. Shell rather thin, dextral, trochiform in immature individuals, more regularly rounded in mature specimens. Spire conical, with 5–6 flat-sided, slightly inflated whorls; body whorl commonly, but not invariably, strongly angulated below middle. Surface marked with fine growth lines and commonly with fine revolving lines. Aperture subquadrate to round-ovate.

Types. Hypotypes, O.S.U. Nos. 20861, 20864, 20865, 20870, 20871

	Length	*Width*	*Ap. Length*	*Ap. Width*	*No. of Whorls*
Hypotype, No. 20861	22 mm	14	12	14	4.5
Hypotype, No. 20864	29	19	..	..	5.5
Hypotype, No. 20865	25	18	..	..	5
Hypotype, No. 20870	14	12	..	..	3.5
Hypotype, No. 20871	23	17	12	9	5

Occurrence. In central Utah, the species is confined to the lower part of the Flagstaff, although stray shells and fragments are occasionally found in the middle part of the Flagstaff. In the upper part of the formation it is totally absent and is replaced by *V. paludinae-formis* (Hall). The data for 24 collections, out of a possible 42, are as follows: coll. 3*, 7 specimens; coll. 5*, 1 specimen; coll. 7*, 7 specimens; coll. 8*, 4 specimens; coll. 10*, 5 specimens, *I*—13.9 per cent, *V*—46.6 per cent; coll. 11*, 7 specimens; coll. 12, 103 specimens, *I*—81.1 per cent, *V*—76.2 per cent; coll. 13, 109 specimens, *I*—7.1 per cent, *V*—34.5 per cent; coll. 16, 24 specimens, *I*—1.7 per cent, *V*—49.1 per cent; coll. 20, 66 specimens, *I*—3.7 per cent, *V*—23.6 per cent; coll. 21*, 1 specimen; coll. 22*, 1 specimen; coll. 25*, 4 specimens; coll. 30*, 4 specimens; coll. 31*, 3 specimens; coll. 32*, 2 specimens; coll. 33*, 12 specimens; coll. 34, 3 specimens, *I*—0.9 per cent, *V*—19.1 per cent; coll. 35, 12 specimens, *I*—6.9 per cent, *V*—25.0 per cent; coll. 36*, 4 specimens; coll. 41, 1 specimen, *I*—0.2 per cent, *V*—11.8 per cent; coll. 42*, 13 specimens; coll. 43, 5 specimens, *I*—9.4 per cent, *V*—86.7 per cent; coll. 53*, 12 specimens.

Henderson (1935, p. 175) summarizes the range from the extensive literature as follows:

"Originally described from the Fort Union Eocene, ten miles below Fort Union (now Fort Buford), North Dakota, this species (with unnamed varieties) has since been reported from the Eocene and Upper Cretaceous of North Dakota, Montana, Wyoming, Utah, Colorado, New Mexico, and British America. Some or all of the Cretaceous records, especially those designated Laramie, should be referred to the Eocene, as now understood."

Yen (1948b, p. 36, 40) records the species from the Tongue River member of the Fort Union formation (Paleocene) and from the lowest unit of the Wasatch formation (lower Eocene) of southern Montana.

Remarks. The species is easily distinguished in spite of minor variations in shell form. Specimens with a strongly angulated body whorl are easily distinguished from *V. paludinae-formis* (Hall) which invariably has a rounded body whorl; specimens without angulation of the body whorl exhibit basal angulation in some part of the spire, and this gives the spire a squat appearance very different from that of *V. paludinaeformis* (Hall). Records of *V. trochiformis* from the upper part of the Flagstaff, especially in the Gunnison Plateau and in central Utah outside of the Wasatch Plateau, are almost certainly based either on misidentification of *V. paludinaeformis* or of a bulimoid land snail to be described later in this paper. When large series of the three species are compared, the differences between them are easily appreciated, and correct assignment is possible. Yen (1948b, p. 40; Pl. 10, figs. 1–5) has shown the differences between *V. trochiformis, V. raynoldsanus* (Meek and Hayden), and *V. retusus* (Meek and Hayden). *V. trochiformis* is equally distinct from other Paleocene species.

The species forms a major element of the fauna of the lower part of the Flagstaff, especially in volume; it is overshadowed in numbers of individuals by *Hydrobia utahensis* and in some collections even by *Micropyrgus minutulus*.

The specimens in my collections agree well with C. A. White's (U. S. National Museum, 8598, 8601, 20079), which I have seen. His lot 8598 is labelled "Laramie/ E. side of Joe's Valley/ Utah"; Joe's Valley is in the Wasatch Plateau. Lot 8601 is labelled "Laramie/ Last Bluff Ephraim City. S. of Last Bluff/ Utah". These specimens were too poorly preserved to measure, but they exhibit undoubted lower Flagstaff preservation. His lot 20079 is labelled "Eocene, Wasatch Gr./ Wales/ Utah", which is undoubtedly an error. The specimens have the same preservation as those from the lower part of the Flagstaff and were undoubtedly derived from that part of the formation—which does not occur in Wales Canyon or anywhere else along the Gunnison Plateau. No doubt they were either from float blocks picked up near Wales or else the locality "Wales" is a general one, possibly referring to the part of the Wasatch Plateau opposite the town of Wales. The town of Wales is much closer to the Gunnison Plateau, but in White's day it may have been the only convenient geographic feature to which collections could be referred.

Viviparus paludinaeformis (Hall), 1845
(Pl. 2, figs. 10–13)

Turbo paludinaeformis HALL, 1845, Fremont's Exped. Rocky Mts., Ore. and N. Calif., p. 309, Pl. 3, fig. 13
Viviparus paludinaeformis MEEK, 1870, Hayden Surv., 4th Ann. Rept., p. 299, 314
Viviparus paludinaeformis HENDERSON, 1935, Geol. Soc. Am., Spec. Paper 3, p. 171 (extensive bibliography)

Diagnosis. Shell large, of about 4 whorls, rapidly and regularly enlarging, regularly inflated and without angulation. Surface marked by fine axial striae which arch forward toward aperture; aperture oval, its apical portion bluntly pointed; umbilicus closed.

Types. Hypotypes, O.S.U. Nos. 20866, 20867, 20884, 20885

	Height	*Width*	*Ap. Height*	*Ap. Width*	*No. of Whorls*
Hypotype, No. 20866	29 mm	18	12	10	4.5
Hypotype, No. 20867	29	19	15	13	4.5
Hypotype, No. 20884	11	9	..	..	4
Hypotype, No. 20885	21	12	11	7	4

Occurrence. Upper part of Flagstaff formation, at 6 out of 7 localities: coll. 1, 17 specimens, *I*—5.3 per cent, *V*—11.9 per cent; coll. 2*, 46 specimens; coll. 29, 10 specimens, *I*—4.2 per cent, *V*—8.6 per cent; coll. 38*, 6 specimens; coll. 40*, 27 specimens; coll. 45*, 250 specimens. In central Utah, the species is found only in the upper part of the Flagstaff. Henderson summarizes its range as follows: "Known only from the Eocene and Paleocene of western Wyoming and northwestern Colorado." The records cited extend the range to hte Eocene of central Utah. Yen (1948b) did not find the species in the Paleocene and basal Eocene of Montana.

Remarks. This species is easily distinguished from *Viviparus trochiformis* (White) by the shape of its whorls, which are regularly inflated and lack the basal angulation of White's species. White (1877, p. 611) had already noted that *V. paludinaeformis* ". . . is a constant associate of *G. tenera* and at none of the localities where I have collected these two species have I ever found either of them unaccompanied by the other." This statement applies throughout the upper part of the Flagstaff, where the two species appear together or not at all. In the overlying Colton formation of central Utah, *Goniobasis tenera* is commonly the only mollusk found in beds that contain not a single specimen of *V. paludinaeformis*. The association of the two species in appreciable numbers is a good indication that the beds in which they appear are upper Flagstaff.

Genus **Lioplacodes** Meek, 1864

Diagnosis. Shell oblong-ovate, whorls gently convex, sutures well impressed; aperture elongate-ovate to pyriform, inner margin thickened; ornamentation of fine to coarse axial striae, in some but not all species crossed by a few spiral cords; operculum unknown. *Type:* *L. veternus* (Meek and Hayden)

Ecology. The genus is extinct but closely related, at least in characteristics of the shell, to the living genus *Lioplax*. Any conclusions derived from *Lioplax* would be highly conjectural, for *Lioplax* lives under conditions very different from those in central Utah in Paleocene time. The Flagstaff specimens occur in sufficient numbers to indicate that the 3 species of that formation were lacustrine forms, living in shallow quiet water in the company of a molluscan fauna in which operculate gill-breathers were dominant. Its occurrence is rather erratic and limited, which suggests that *Lioplacodes* was less tolerant of varied ecologic conditions than some of its associates. The species of the Flagstaff formation are nevertheless members of a vigorous stock, as indicated by their abundance in certain beds. Their most constant associates are *Hydrobia utahensis* and *Pleurolimnaea tenuicosta,* but all the other species of the lower part of the Flagstaff may occur with it also. Living *Lioplax* prefers a mud bottom in about 1 m of water (Baker, 1928, p. 51) but has also been found in shallower water and on sand, gravel, and boulder bottoms, both in lakes and in the quiet parts of rivers.

Remarks. Yen's recent descriptions of several new species of *Lioplacodes* show that the genus ranges from the Triassic to the Paleocene. Species of the genus are easily distinguished from *viviparus* by their smaller size and more elongate spire; from *Goniobasis* they differ in being narrower, in having fewer whorls, and in having much more subdued ornamentation, especially in the earlier whorls, than *Goniobasis.*

Lioplacodes limnaeiformis (Meek and Hayden), 1856

(Pl. 2, figs. 14, 15)

Bulimus limnaeiformis MEEK AND HAYDEN, 1856, Phila. Acad. Nat. Sci., Proc., vol. 8, p. 118, 278

Thaumastus limnaeiformis WHITE, 1883, Am. Jour. Sci., 3d ser., vol. 26, p. 122

Campeloma limnaeiformis RUSSELL, 1929, Roy. Soc. Canada, Trans., vol. 23, p. 81–83, Pl. 1, figs. 1–3

Lioplax limnaeiformis RUSSELL, *in* JEPSEN, 1930, Am. Phil. Soc., Proc., vol. 69, p. 498

Campeloma limnaeformis (Meek and Hayden) HENDERSON, 1935, Geol. Soc. Am., Spec. Paper 3, p. 179 (extensive bibliography)

Lioplacodes limnaeiformis YEN, 1948, U. S. Geol. Surv., Prof. Paper 214-C, p. 41, Pl. 10, fig. 11

Diagnosis. Spire slender as compared with other species of the genus; whorls not inflated; aperture elongate-oval; ornamentation of axial striae only.

Types. Hypotypes, O. S. U. Nos. 20863, 20887

	Height	Width	Ap. Height	Ap. Width	No. of Whorls
Hypotype, No. 20863	12 mm	5	5	2	..
Hypotype, No. 20887	12	6	5	2	5

Occurrence. Lower part of Flagstaff, in 2 of 42 collections: coll. 20, 10 specimens, *I*—0.6 per cent, *V*—0.9 per cent; coll. 42*, 1 specimen. This is the rarest of the species of *Lioplacodes* in the Flagstaff formation. It occurs in very small numbers with *L. mariana* Yen and *L. tenuicarinata* (Meek and Hayden) for reasons which are obscure at present. Yen (1946, p. 41) records it from the Fort Union, probably of Montana, but without locality.

Remarks. This species is easily distinguished from both *L. mariana* Yen and *L. tenuicarinata* (Meek and Hayden) by its slender spire and uninflated whorls. It is closest to *L. mariana* in form, but it does not appear to be an extreme variant of that species, for it occurs with it in small numbers and without intergrades, at least in the lower part of the Flagstaff.

Lioplacodes mariana Yen, 1946

(Pl. 2, figs. 16–18)

Lioplacodes mariana YEN 1946, Am. Jour. Sci., vol. 244, no. 1, p. 44, Pl. 1, figs. 5a–c; 1948, U. S. Geol. Surv., Prof. Paper 214–C, p. 41, Pl. 10, figs. 6, 6a–c

Diagnosis. Shell oblong-ovate, spire turreted; whorls gently convex; sculpture of distinct axial and spiral striae; aperture pyriform, inner margin slightly thickened; inner lip oblique and nearly straight at the columella.

Types. Hypotypes, O.S.U. Nos. 20877, 20878, 20886

	Height	Width	Ap. Height	Ap. Width	No. of Whorls
Hypotype, No. 20877	20 mm	9	7	5	4.5
Hypotype, No. 20878	14	8	6	5	5.5
Hypotype, No. 20886	16	9	6	5	4

Occurrence. Lower part of Flagstaff formation, 11 of 42 collections: coll. 7*, 7 specimens; coll. 8*, 7 specimens; coll. 12, 10 specimens, *I*—7.9 per cent, *V*—2.0 per cent; coll. 13, 3 specimens, *I*—0.2 per cent, *V*—0.3 per cent; coll. 16, 6 specimens, *I*—0.4 per cent, *V*—3.3 per cent; coll. 20, 456 specimens, *I*—25.7 per cent, *V*—38.5 per cent; coll. 21*, 6 specimens; coll. 30*, 14 specimens; coll. 34, 32 specimens, *I*—9.0 per cent, *V*—54.2 per cent; coll. 35, 98 specimens, *I*—56.3 per cent, *V*—54.3 per cent; coll. 46, 1 specimen, *I*—0.3 per cent, *V*—8.2 per cent. This is the most abundant of the three species of *Lioplacodes* in our collections. It is not present in all collections, but wherever it is found, it outnumbers *L. tenuicarinata* by about 3 to 2 and the rare *L. limnaeiformis* by more than 100 to 1. There seems to be little variation in the abundance of the species from the bottom to the top of the lower part of the Flagstaff but, in central Utah at least, the species is not found above that part of the formation. It was originally described by Yen from the Paleocene Fort Union, just below the Arvada coal bed, Sheridan County, Wyoming. Yen (1946, p. 41) also records it from the Paleocene and lowest Eocene of Montana.

Remarks. This species is distinguished from *L. limnaeiformis* (Meek and Hayden) by its more inflated whorls and consequently wider spire; it differs from *L. tenuicarinata* (Meek and Hayden) in having less well-developed spiral striae; in *L. tenuicarinata* some of the striae are so strong as to deserve description as raised cords or subdued carinae, in which case they are associated with a slight angulation of the whorls; between the raised cords are other, smaller, spiral striae. *L. mariana* in some cases has spiral striae, but they are all of nearly equal development, do not assume the character of cords, do not persist on the body whorl, and are not associated with angulation of the spire.

Lioplacodes tenuicarinata (Meek and Hayden), 1857
(Pl. 2, figs. 19-22)

Melania tenuicarinata MEEK AND HAYDEN, 1857, Phila. Acad. Nat. Sci., Proc., vol. 9, p. 137

Goniobasis tenuicarinata MEEK, 1876, Hayden Surv., Mon. 9, p. 566, Pl. 43, fig. 14

Goniobasis (Lioplax?) tenuicarinata WHITE, 1883, U.S. Geol. Surv., 3d Ann. Rept., p. 463, 476, Pl. 26, fig. 11

Goniobasis tenuicarinata Meek and Hayden, HENDERSON 1935, Geol. Soc. Am., Spec. Paper 3, p. 229

Lioplacodes tenuicarinata YEN, 1948, U. S. Geol. Surv., Prof. Paper 214–C, p. 40, Pl. 10, figs. 7, 7a–d

Diagnosis. Shell ovate, conical; spire turreted, with 5–6 gently convex whorls and a well-defined suture; aperture elongate-ovate; surface marked with fine to coarse axial striae, crossed by spiral striae and cords of varying strength; commonly one of the spiral cords is stronger than the others and corresponds to an angulation of the whorl.

Types. Hypotypes, O.S.U. Nos. 20859, 20868, 20869

	Height	Width	Ap. Height	Ap. Width	No. of Whorls
Hypotype, No. 20859	17 mm	8	7	6	5
Hypotype, No. 20868	19	10	..	..	4.5
Hypotype, No. 20869	22	10	..	..	5.5

Occurrence. Lower part of Flagstaff formation, 12 of 42 collections: coll. 5*, 5 specimens; coll. 12, 6 specimens, I—4.7 per cent, V—1.2 per cent; coll. 13, 3 specimens, I—0.2 per cent, V—0.3 per cent; coll. 17, 3 specimens, I—1.0 per cent, V—7.9 per cent; coll. 20, 199 specimens, I—11.3 per cent, V—17.0 per cent; coll. 21*, 3 specimens; coll. 24, 4 specimens, I—0.3 per cent, V—8.7 per cent; coll. 34, 4 specimens, I—1.2 per cent, V—6.8 per cent; coll. 35, 23 specimens, I—13.2 per cent, V—12.8 per cent; coll. 36*, 9 specimens; coll. 42*, 5 specimens; coll. 47, 5 specimens, I—2.1 per cent, V—25.7 per cent. This species is somewhat less abundant than *L. mariana* in the basal part of the Flagstaff formation; the ratio between the two species is about 3.4 to 2. The two species occur together in nearly all collections of any size; where one is absent and the other present, the collection is usually small, and the presence of only one of these species is probably due to insufficient collecting. The species, like *L. mariana,* appears to be confined to the lower part of the Flagstaff. Yen (1948b, p. 36) records it from the Paleocene and basal Eocene of Montana. Henderson (1935, p. 228) places the species in the genus *Goniobasis* and summarizes the records up to 1935. From his summary (1935, p. 229–230) it would appear that the species ranges from the Cretaceous (Laramie, Mesaverde, Lance, Edmonton) to the Eocene (Fort Union, Torrejon, etc.), but it is likely that many of these records are based on misidentifications.

Remarks. The species is most easily confused with *L. mariana* Yen, which it resembles in size and in character of the whorls. It is distinguished from that species by the possession of persistent spiral cords which may approach the distinctness of carinae or may be obscure and no more than strong spiral lines. Inconspicuous spiral striae are present on some specimens of *L. mariana,* but they do not persist on the body whorl which has axial striae only. In *L. tenuicarinata,* at least one, in some cases several, of the spiral cords are prominent and persistent on all whorls. The most prominent of the spiral cords is commonly the one on the shoulder of the whorl, in which case the angulation of the whorl is very prominent. In some specimens, the shoulder of the whorl is without a cord or has a poorly developed axial stria; in these specimens, the angulation of the whorl is less prominent but sufficiently well developed to be apparent even in cursory examination. The angulation of the whorl and the persistent spiral striae provide the best criteria for distinguishing this species from *L. mariana.* The spire of *L. limnaeiformis* is so much more slender than that of either *L. tenuicarinata* or *L. mariana* that it can be recognized at a glance from these species.

Family PLEUROCERIDAE

Genus **Goniobasis** Lea, 1862

Diagnosis. Shell dextral, elongate-turreted to ovate-conic, many whorls; axially plicate, spirally striate, tuberculate, or smooth; thick and solid; aperture subrhomboidal, subangular at base but not canaliculate; columella smooth, not twisted; lip simple, acute. *Type: Melania osculata* Lea.

Ecology. Species of the genus are numerous and widespread in the living fauna of North America. Their metropolis is in the southeastern United States, an area from which a vast number of species has been described. Calvin Goodrich, the leading specialist in Pleuroceridae, has reduced a considerable number of the species of earlier authors to synonymy, but a sufficient number of valid forms still remains to demonstrate the greater abundance of species in the states south of the Ohio River and east of the Mississippi. Species become progressively fewer north of the Ohio River and west of the Mississippi. Their ecological preferences are as varied as the characteristics of the species. They have been found in lakes and rivers, on sand, mud, and boulder bottoms, in swift and quiet waters. Goodrich (1945, p. 26) summarizes the habitats for a single species, *G. livescens* (Menke) and has discussed the habitat of many others in his other papers. Species of *Goniobasis* have even been found in springs and in the outlet of artesian wells, for example *G. laurae, G. interioris* (Goodrich, 1944). This does not mean that all species are able to adapt to environment without regard to varying conditions. Certain species are restricted to a particular river drainage; others have succeeded in establishing themselves in several, and still others are restricted to a particular small stream or a portion of a river.

Some species, at least, of living *Goniobasis* show remarkable tolerance of environmental conditions. *G. virginica* (Gmelin) has been taken in tidal pools of the Raritan River, New Jersey; the same species tolerates alternating fresh-water and saline conditions (Goodrich, 1945, p. 28). Bailey (1929) has collected it in the Gunpowder River, Maryland, where the salinity is 50 per cent of that of the ocean. Goodrich also reports that *Goniobasis* in general can tolerate a wide range of turbidity and silting and even pollution by domestic sewage. Where the snail finds sufficiently favorable conditions, it establishes large colonies, and its occurrence is usually described as "common," "abundant," and "very abundant." Its habit of attaching the egg masses to stones, sticks, dead clam shells, or other pleurocerids considerably restricts its ability to disperse. Goodrich (1944, p. 7) has pointed out that it is not known to be carried by wildfowl or beetles, and that it cannot be carried from one drainage system into another unless the object to which it is attached is carried also.

The Flagstaff species is undoubtedly lacustrine. Its stratigraphic distribution indicates that it was able to invade the Central Utah area at least four times and to establish large colonies each time.

Remarks. The Flagstaff material assigned to this genus exhibits considerable variation but can be placed in one species, *Goniobasis tenera* (Hall). Reference to *Goniobasis* is somewhat insecure, as all such generic assignments must be in the absence of soft parts, but it ap-

pears preferable to placing these specimens in *Pleurocera,* since the columella in these specimens is not twisted. An added bit of evidence is that the ornamentation in the specimens agrees
with that of living western species of *Goniobasis,* for example *G. plicifera* (Lea).

Goniobasis tenera (Hall), 1845
(Pl. 2, figs. 23–39)

Cerithium tenerum HALL, 1845, Rept. Fremont's Exped. Ore. and N. Calif., p. 308, Pl. 3, fig. 6
Goniobasis tenera Hall sp., MEEK, 1870, Hayden Surv., 4th Ann. Rept., p. 298
Goniobasis tenera tenera (Hall) HENDERSON, 1935, Geol. Soc. Am., Spec. Paper 3, p. 226

Diagnosis. Shell elongate, of about 10–12 whorls. Whorls convex, ornamented with strong,
rounded to subarcuate carinae; suture strongly impressed. Apical whorls marked by strong
spiral carinae and axial plications, both of which may be subobsolete in mature shell. Aperture ovate, a little longer than wide.

Types and dimensions. See G. tenera forms A–D

Occurrence. In the Flagstaff formation, *Goniobasis tenera* (Hall) is found in the basal
and upper parts of the formation and is absent from the middle part. It also occurs in the
Colton formation but not in the North Horn and Green River formations of central Utah.
The specimens from the two parts of the Flagstaff and the Colton are obviously referable to
a single species. They vary considerably in detail of ornamentation, especially in the obsoles-
cence of the axial plications in the mature shell. In spite of these variations, it is possible to
recognize distinct forms which are most abundant at a particular level but are accompanied
by variants which approach the forms found most abundantly at other levels. These forms
may be segregated because of their stratigraphic value, but taxonomically they are so closely
related that they are not worthy of even varietal or subspecific rank. All four forms are therefore assigned to a single species and distinguished by the letters A, B, C, and D. Detailed
records of their occurrence are given under each form.

Henderson (1935, p. 226) gives the records of this species and its subspecies in the literature and notes that ". . . some of the forms listed as subspecies herein may be distinct species."
That is possible, but it should be pointed out that with such a variable species, isolated specimens present a semblance of distinctness which vanishes when larger suites are examined.
The species has been recorded from the Eocene of the southwest, but some of the records
may be Paleocene. Yen (1948b) did not find the species in the Paleocene of Montana; it appears to be replaced by *G. nebrascensis* (Meek and Hayden) and *G. nebrascensis producta*
(White), which are devoid of axial plications and spiral carinae.

Remarks. At first sight, collections of this species seem to be indistinguishable from each
other; it is only when large series, including immature specimens, are examined that a pattern becomes apparent. The ornamentation, both axial and spiral, is developed very early;
ephebic and gerontic variation in ornamentation is a development, either in the direction of
attenuation or diversification, of a primitively strong and well-established norm. These specimens also demonstrate the surprisingly large number of whorls in this species; a specimen
scarcely more than 3 mm long exhibits 7 whorls, and 12 whorls is probably the usual number
for a complete adult shell.

The occurrence of *Goniobasis tenera* (Hall) at three distinct and widely separated levels in
the Flagstaff and Colton formations indicates three separate invasions, perhaps four, of that
species into the central Utah area, probably from the same source. The differentiation into
four distinct forms may be taken as the result of evolution over a period of time which is
undetermined but probably lengthy, as it extends over the latest Paleocene and part of the
Eocene. The source whence these forms came is not known, but the most likely location is
the Uinta Basin to the north of central Utah where North Horn, Flagstaff, and Colton
equivalents exist but have not as yet been defined.

In the earliest form to invade the central Utah area, form A, the ornamentation pattern
of the apical whorls is preserved throughout the development of the shell, save for the accentu-
ation of the middle carina which results in the formation of nodes on the body whorl where the

carina crosses a plication. Its representatives are found in the basal part of the Flagstaff formation. An early variant, form D, also penetrated into the area in Flagstaff time, probably a little later than form A, judging by its stratigraphic position, or evolved from form A in the Flagstaff lake. In this form the originally strong plications are attenuated early in the development of the shell, and they are almost entirely absent in adult specimens. The spiral carinae persist over the entire shell but remain of approximately equal size. In the upper part of the Flagstaff another form, form B, appears, which is more closely related to form A in ornamental pattern. In it, plications and spiral carinae persist throughout the development of the shell, but nodes do not develop along the middle of the body whorl as in form A. A few specimens of the upper part of the Flagstaff nevertheless are similar to form A or form D. In the Colton form, form C, plications and nodes are the dominant ornamentation, and carinae appear only on the body whorl. The four forms may be distinguished by the following characteristics:

Form	Plications	Nodes	Carinae	Stratigraphic Position
A	Strong	On body whorl only	On base of whorl only but may be poorly developed on entire whorl	Lower part of Flagstaff
B	Strong	None	On whole whorl	Upper part of Flagstaff
C	Strong	On all whorls	On base of whorl only	Colton
D	Weak to absent on body whorl	None	On whole whorl	Lower part of Flagstaff

Goniobasis tenera (Hall), form A
(Pl. 2, figs. 23–27)

Diagnosis. Shell elongate, of about 10–12 whorls; suture strongly impressed, whorls convex, with strong, rounded to subacute carinae. Apical portion of immature shell marked by both strong spiral carinae and axial plications; axial plications weaker and restricted to the central part of the whorl, assuming the appearance of nodes on younger whorls of mature shell.

Types. Hypotypes, O.S.U. Nos. 20888–91, 20905

	Height	Width	Ap. Height	Ap. Width	No. of Whorls
Hypotype, No. 20888	28 mm	11	..	..	9
Hypotype, No. 20889	22	7	..	..	10
Hypotype, No. 20890	5.6	2	1.6	1	5.5
Hypotype, No. 20891	4.1	1.6	1	1	5
Hypotype, No. 20905	24	9	..	..	10
Mature specimen	26	10	6	4	7
Mature specimen	24	10	7	5	6
Mature specimen	20	11	8	7	3
Mature specimen	19	9	6	5	4

(Four mature specimens other than the hypotypes)

Occurrence. This form is found only in the basal part of the Flagstaff formation, in 7 of 42 localities: coll. 9*, 12 specimens; coll. 10*, 10 specimens; coll. 16, 17 specimens, I—1.2 per cent, V—17.3 per cent; coll. 20, 23 specimens, I—1.3 per cent, V—3.6 per cent; coll. 30*, 1 specimen; coll. 31*, 15 specimens; coll. 34, 1 specimen, I—0.3 per cent, V—3.2 per cent.

Remarks. In each of these lots, some specimens are closely similar to form B, in that the nodes are more strongly developed than usual; others are similar to form C, in that the carinae are more subdued than in other specimens. These extreme variants are in the minority in a collection of any size, forming less than 5 per cent of any given collection. Their presence is emphasized here so that unfounded stratigraphic assignments may be guarded against. Because of the variability of the species and the presence in a given lot of extreme variants, stratigraphic assignments should not be made on the basis of this species unless a number of specimens, at least 25 or 30, are available for study. The presence of extreme variants does not invalidate the use of the species as a stratigraphic marker providing these precautions are taken.

Goniobasis tenera (Hall), form B
(Pl. 2, figs. 28–30)

Diagnosis. Shell elongate, of about 10–12 whorls; suture strongly impressed; whorls convex, each marked by strong axial plications intersected by strong spiral carinae; aperture ovate and a little longer than wide.

Types. Hypotypes, O.S.U. Nos. 20892, 20893, 20894

	Height	*Width*	*Ap. Height*	*Ap. Width*	*No. of Whorls*
Hypotype, No. 20892	37 mm	9	..	..	11
Hypotype, No. 20893	21	7	6	4	8
Hypotype, No. 20894	18	6	..	..	8
unfigured specimen	29.0	11.0	5.0	5.0	6
unfigured specimen	26.5	12.0	5.0	5.0	6
unfigured specimen	22.0	7.0	4.0	4.5	7
unfigured specimen	21.0	8.0	6.0	4.0	5
unfigured specimen	16.0	7.0	4.0	3.0	6
unfigured specimen	14.5	6.0	4.0	3.0	5

Occurrence. Upper part of Flagstaff formation, in 5 of 7 collections: coll. 1, 50 specimens, I—15.6 per cent V—17.5 per cent; coll. 29, 73 specimens, I—30.9 per cent, V—31.2 per cent; coll. 38*, 7 specimens; coll. 40*, 83 specimens; coll. 45, 80 specimens.

Remarks. This form also includes extreme variants which can easily be confused with forms A or C. The same remarks made under form A concerning caution in stratigraphic assignment apply here also.

Goniobasis tenera (Hall), form C
(Pl. 2, figs. 31–34)

Diagnosis. Shell as in forms A and B except for the following details of ornamentation: axial plications are strongly produced on entire shell, but strong spiral carinae are present only on base of whorl.

Types. Hypotypes, O.S.U. Nos. 20895, 20897, 20898, 20899

	Height	*Width*	*Ap. Height*	*Ap. Width*	*No. of Whorls*
Hypotype, No. 20895	29 mm	10	..	..	9
Hypotype, No. 20897	32	11	7	6	9
Hypotype, No. 20898	30	8	6	5	9
Hypotype, No. 20899	28	11	7	6	9

Occurrence. This form is characteristic of the basal beds of the Colton formation at many localities both in the Wasatch and Gunnison plateaus. It is included here because of its intimate relationship with the other three forms of *G. tenera* (Hall) and the importance of distinguishing all four for stratigraphic purposes.

Remarks. This form is extremely abundant in some of the lacustrine beds of the Colton formation not far above the *Goniobasis*-bearing beds of the Flagstaff. In each of the localities where it was collected, form C occurred above the first red bed above the Flagstaff; the latter is generally accepted as the contact between the Flagstaff and the Colton. As indicated earlier, it probably represents the last invasion of the *Goniobasis tenera* stock into the central Utah area from the same source which supplied the two or three earlier invasions.

Goniobasis tenera (Hall), form D
(Pl. 2, figs. 35–39)

Diagnosis. Shell as in forms A and B except for the following details of ornamentation: axial plications weak throughout, absent on body whorl in some specimens; no nodes on body whorl; carinae equally developed on all whorls.

Types. Hypotypes, O.S.U. Nos. 20900–20904

	Height	Width	Ap. Height	Ap. Width	No. of Whorls
Hypotype, No. 20900	7 mm	1.7	..	..	5
Hypotype, No. 20901	12	6	..	..	7
Hypotype, No. 20902	31	9	..	..	..
Hypotype, No. 20903	25	9	5	5	8.5
Hypotype, No. 20904	32	8	6	5	9

Occurrence. Lower part of Flagstaff formation, at 1 of 42 localities: coll. 20, 64 specimens, I—3.6 per cent, V—10.3 per cent.

Remarks. This form is the farthest removed in its final expression from the typical pattern present on the early whorls of *G. tenera*. The axial plications are almost entirely suppressed, and the carinae are strongly developed on all whorls. It would be tempting to set it aside as a distinct species were it not for its obvious relationships with *G. tenera,* as exemplified in the early whorls, and its occurrence with form A in the same collection.

Family AMNICOLIDAE
Genus **Hydrobia** Hartmann, 1821

Diagnosis. Shell dextral, small, elongate, conical, subacute; whorls 5–8, slightly convex; sutures impressed; aperture oval; lip simple, sharp; ornamentation of fine, crowded axial striae; umbilicus slightly open. *Type: Hydrobia ventrosa* Mont.

Ecology. Since the generic reference of the species is rather insecure, it would be fruitless to review here the ecological preferences of living species of *Hydrobia*. If numbers of individuals present in a collection are any indication of habitat preference, it would seem that *H. utahensis* found optimum environmental conditions in the early Flagstaff lake, for this species is found in more collections and in larger numbers than any other of the same age. On the other hand, the other two species of the genus are much scarcer. This rarity seems to indicate, in the case of *H.* cf. *H. recta* White, that its requirements were different from those of *H. utahensis*. The species from the upper part of the Flagstaff is also much less common than *H. utahensis,* but it lived in a different environment, so that not much can be said about it except perhaps that the late Flagstaff lake had less vegetation in it than its predecessor.

Remarks. Two species assigned to this genus occur in the lower part of the Flagstaff and one in the upper. They are among the most abundant gastropods in the lower part of the Flagstaff and outnumber others, although their volume is not great. These species are assigned to *Hydrobia* Hartmann, following Pilsbry (1934, p. 559), rather than to *Paludestrina* d'Orbigny. Their relationship with living *Hydrobia* is somewhat doubtful.

Hydrobia utahensis White, 1876
(Pl. 3, figs. 1–4)

Hydrobia utahensis WHITE, 1876, Geol. Uinta Mts., p. 103, 132
Bythinella utahensis WHITE, 1877, Hayden Surv., Bull. 3, p. 611
Hydrobia utahensis HENDERSON, 1935, Geol. Soc. Am., Spec. Paper 3, p. 199

Diagnosis. Shell small, elongate, conical, with moderately long spire; sides nearly straight. Whorls 6–7 with an impressed suture. Aperture ovate, a little longer than wide; inferior margin slightly angular, upper margin evenly rounded. Surface marked with fine, subobsolete lines of growth.

Types. Hypotypes, O.S.U. Nos. 20930–20933

	Height	Width	Ap. Height	Ap. Width	No. of Whorls
Holotype, USNM	5 mm	2.0	..	..	6
Hypotype, No. 20930	4	2.3	1	1.3	5
Hypotype, No. 20931	4.3	2	..	..	5
Hypotype, No. 20932	4	2	1	1	5.5
Hypotype, No. 20933	3.3	1.6	..	..	5
Unnumbered specimen	4.5	1.8	1.2	1.1	6
Unnumbered specimen	4.9	2.0	1.5	1.3	5
Unnumbered specimen	4.5	2.0	1.3	1.2	5
Unnumbered specimen	4.0	1.9	1.4	0.8	5

Occurrence. Lower part of Flagstaff, in 27 of 42 collections: coll. 3*, 3 specimens; coll. 9*, 33 specimens; coll. 10*, 15 specimens; coll. 13, 1315 specimens, *I*—86.0 per cent, *V*—3.4 per cent; coll. 15*, 39 specimens; coll. 16, 1272 specimens, *I*—88.8 per cent, *V*—20.8 per cent; coll. 17, 272 specimens, *I*—90.8 per cent, *V*—21.4 per cent; coll. 18, 208 specimens, *I*—91.1 per cent, *V*—75.8 per cent; coll. 19*, 31 specimens; coll. 20, 566 specimens, *I*—32.0 per cent, *V*—1.5 per cent; coll. 21*, 44 specimens; coll. 22*, 21 specimens; coll. 23*, 2 specimens; coll. 24, 1297 specimens, *I*—97.6 per cent, *V*—84.8 per cent; coll. 25*, 15 specimens; coll. 26*, 103 specimens; coll. 30*, 10 specimens; coll. 31*, 16 specimens; coll. 33*, 41 specimens; coll. 34, 291 specimens, *I*—82.2 per cent, *V*—14.8 per cent; coll. 35, 40 specimens, *I*—23.0 per cent, *V*—0.7 per cent; coll. 36*, 40 specimens; coll. 41, 532 specimens, *I*—89.1 per cent, *V*—50.4 per cent; coll. 42*, 22 specimens; coll. 43, 45 specimens, *I*—84.9 per cent, *V*—6.2 per cent; coll. 46, 284 specimens, *I*—87.4 per cent, *V*—70.4 per cent; coll. 47, 189 specimens, *I*—81.2 per cent, *V*—29.2 per cent.

White's specimens were collected from "Bitter Creek group, Tertiary, west base of Mu-si-ni-a Plateau, Utah, 1,000 feet below summit." If Musinia Peak was meant, as might reasonably be supposed from White's revised wording of the locality in U. S. Geol. Survey Bulletin 34 ("west base of Musinia" etc.), the locality and stratigraphic position of the types could be fixed exactly. I have collected *H. utahensis* from the east flank of Musinia Peak (colls. 46 and 47 of this paper) where the lower part of the Flagstaff formation is indeed about 1,000 feet below the summit of the peak. On the other hand, if the "Mu-si-ni-a Plateau" of the original description referred to the Wasatch Plateau, more than a dozen localities could satisfy the conditions imposed. I have seen the type of *H. utahensis* White; judging from the lithology of the specimen, its mode of preservation, and its exact agreement with my collections, I am certain that White's specimens came from the basal part of the Flagstaff formation in the Wasatch Plateau and that they are therefore Paleocene and not Eocene as has been suggested by Henderson (1935, p. 199).

Remarks. The Utah records of this species need revision, but material is not at present available for positive statements concerning all of them. It can be stated that no material certainly identifiable with this species has been found outside of the basal part of the Flagstaff formation. A closely related species, *Hydrobia recta* White occurs in the North Horn formation and doubtfully in the basal Flagstaff; Yen (1946, p. 45) has described *H. victa* from the Paleocene of Sheridan County, Wyoming, a species which differs in being larger and in having more convex whorls.

In all the Flagstaff sections measured in the Wasatch Plateau, this species is characteristic of the lower part of the formation. It does not occur in the North Horn formation, nor is it found in the upper part of the Flagstaff or in the Colton and Green River formation. If proper care is exercised, the Flagstaff formation of the Wasatch Plateau may be broadly zoned on the occurrence or absence of this species. Wherever found, it is present in large numbers, in some cases alone, in others with other species of *Hydrobia* and *Micropyrgus minutulus* (Meek and Hayden).

The species appears to be sexually dimorphic, as are many living amnicolids. The specimens exhibit much variation of apical angle, but the vast majority of specimens fall into two patterns. Extremes from both these standard patterns are not numerous enough to require explanation other than normal variation. It would be tempting to separate the two main patterns into varieties, but their constant occurrence in nearly equal numbers seems best attributed to sexual dimorphism.

Hydrobia cf. H. recta White, 1876
(Pl. 3, figs. 5–7)

Hydrobia recta WHITE, 1876, Geol. Uinta Mts., p. 103, 132; 1886, Geol. Surv., Bull. 34, p. 12, 30, Pl. 2, fig. 21
Bythinella recta WHITE, 1877, Hayden Surv., Bull. 3, p. 611
Hydrobia recta HENDERSON, 1935, Geol. Soc. Am., Spec. Paper 3, p. 197

Diagnosis. Shell dextral, small, slender; spire acute, with almost straight sides; whorls flat-sided, 7–9, increasing regularly but gradually in size from apex to aperture; aperture ovate; lip simple, acute; surface marked with fine growth lines.

Types. Hypotypes, O.S.U. Nos. 20095, 20935, 20936

	Height	Width	Ap. Height	Ap. Width	No. of Whorls
White's type material	5.5 mm	2	..	..	8
White's type material	5.5	2	..	..	5[1]
Hypotype, No. 20095	4.6	1.6	..	..	6
Hypotype, No. 20935	3.3	1.3	..	..	6.5
Hypotype, No. 20936	5.3	1.6	..	..	8.5
unnumbered specimen	5.5	1.5	..	..	8
unnumbered specimen	5.0	1.7	..	..	7.5
unnumbered specimen	4.5	1.2	..	..	7
unnumbered specimen	4.0	1.2	..	..	6.5

Occurrence. Lower part of Flagstaff formation, 3 of 42 collections: coll. 10*, 1 specimen; coll. 31*, 3 specimens; coll. 34, 18 specimens, I—5.0 per cent, V—0.9 per cent.

Remarks. The identification of these specimens with *H. recta* White is somewhat doubtful. The types which I have seen (U. S. National Museum, No. 12501) came from the "Bitter Creek group, Tert., Almy coal mines, near Evanston, Wyo." (White, 1876b, p. 103, 132), but White later gave more precise data: "Cret., 3 miles from Evanston, Wyo., upper beds at coal mines." The type lot consists of two specimens, each on a small slab of dark brown siltstone; their measurements have been given for comparison with Flagstaff specimens. These show that my specimens are more slender than White's types; in addition, the whorls of the types are more globose than any material I have seen from the Flagstaff. They are related in the generally slender and straight-sided appearance of the shell, and it may well be that more extensive collecting at the type locality would reveal an intergradation between the Wyoming material and mine. I have therefore assigned my Flagstaff specimens to *H. recta* with some doubt.

Hydrobia ephraimensis La Rocque, sp. nov.
(Pl. 3, figs. 8–9)

Description. Shell small, dextral, bluntly conical, narrowly perforate; whorls convex, evenly rounded, suture well impressed. Axial ornamentation of fine crowded striae; no spiral ornamentation. Nuclear whorls small, not flattened on top, smooth. Aperture nearly round, lip sharp.

Types. Holotype, O.S.U. No. 20937; paratypes, O.S.U. Nos. 20938–42

	Height	Width	Ap. Height	Ap. Width	No. of Whorls
Holotype, No. 20937	4.3 mm	1.6	1.3	1.3	5.5
Paratype, No. 20938	2.0	1.1	0.6[2]	0.6[2]	4
Paratype, No. 20939	2.5	1.0	..	..	5
Paratype, No. 20940	1.5	0.75	..	..	3.5
Paratype, No. 20941	1.5	0.75	..	..	3.5
Paratype, No. 20942	1.2	0.6	..	..	3

Occurrence. Upper part of Flagstaff formation, at 1 of 7 localities: coll. 29, 40 specimens, I—16.9 per cent, V—0.3 per cent.

Remarks. This species resembles *H. utahensis* White and *H. victa* Yen (1946, p. 45) but is distinguished from them by its more convex whorls and smaller size. It differs from *H. recta* in its more regular spire with more rapidly increasing whorls; it does not have the subcylindrical outline of *H. recta* and *Micropyrgus minutulus* (Meek and Hayden).

Genus **Micropyrgus** Meek, 1866

Diagnosis. Shell dextral, small, narrowly conical, imperforate, with obtuse apex; body whorl not inflated; aperture rhombic-oval, very narrowly rounded; outer lip thin, simple;

---

[1] Apex missing
[2] Approximate measurements

sutures well impressed, whorls slightly shouldered. *Type: Melania minutula* Meek and Hayden

Ecology. The distinction between *Micropyrgus* and *Hydrobia* is none too convincing, and it can be supposed that these two minute snails were very similar in anatomical features. Both were probably operculate gill-breathers. *Micropyrgus* probably had narrower ecological tolerance than *Hydrobia utahensis* White, for it is not as plentiful in collections. Yet the matrix in which the largest collection of *Micropyrgus* is found appears to be the same sort of dark-gray calcareous shale as all the others.

Remarks. Meek distinguished this genus from *Hydrobia* on the basis of ". . . its more slender form, obtuse apex, convex volutions, and entirely imperforate axis." It contains a single species, *M. minutulus* (Meek and Hayden), which is found in small numbers in the basal part of the Flagstaff formation.

Micropyrgus minutulus (Meek and Hayden), 1856
(Pl. 3, figs. 10–13)

Melania minutula MEEK AND HAYDEN, 1856, Phila. Acad. Nat. Sci., Proc., vol. 8, p. 123, 279
  Melania minitula MEEK AND HAYDEN, 1860, Phila. Acad. Nat. Sci., Proc., vol. 12, p. 430
  Micropyrgus minutulus MEEK, 1876, Hayden Surv., Mon. 9, p. 575, Pl. 43, fig. 18, a, b; WHITE, 1877, Hayden Surv., Bull. 3, p. 613
  Bithinella (Micropyrgus) minutulus TRYON, 1883, Struct. and Syst. Conch., vol. 2, p. 267, Pl. 73, fig. 3
  Micropyrgus minutulus HENDERSON, 1935, Geol. Soc. Am., Spec. Paper 3, p. 201

Diagnosis. Shell dextral, minute, elongate, length about 3 times the width; suture distinctly impressed; whorls 7, slightly convex, increasing gradually from apex; aperture ovate, angular above, slightly flaring below; lip thin, acute, slightly separated from spire on upper and parietal margins. Ornamentation of extremely fine, numerous but not crowded, slightly sinuous growth lines.

Types. U.S.N.M. 2137; Hypotypes, O.S.U. Nos. 20943–46

	Height	Width	Ap. Height	Ap. Width	No. of Whorls
Lectotype, U.S.N.M. 2137[3]	2.5 mm	. .	. .	. .	. .
Hypotype, No. 20943	7	2.3	1.3	1	8.5
Hypotype, No. 20944	7	2.3	1.6	1.3	8.5
Hypotype, No. 20945	5.3	2	1	1	7.5
Hypotype, No. 20946	7	2.3	1.6	1.3	8.5

Occurrence. Lower part of Flagstaff formation, in 11 of 42 collections: coll. 13, 9 specimens, *I*—0.6 per cent, *V*—0.1 per cent; coll. 15*, 3 specimens; coll. 16, 17 specimens, *I*—1.2 per cent, *V*—0.2 per cent; coll. 17, 4 specimens, *I*—1.3 per cent, *V*—0.3 per cent; coll. 18, 8 specimens, *I*—3.5 per cent, *V*—2.4 per cent; coll. 19*, 1 specimen; coll. 20, 262 specimens, *I*—14.8 per cent, *V*—0.7 per cent; coll. 21*, 5 specimens; coll. 39*, 74 specimens; coll. 41, 2 specimens, *I*—0.4 per cent, *V*—0.2 per cent; coll. 46, 16 specimens, *I*—4.9 per cent, *V*—3.3 per cent.

The age of the type specimen was originally given as Miocene, "3 miles below Fort Union," and various authors have referred the beds to the Cretaceous and Eocene. They are either Eocene or Paleocene and probably close to the boundary between the two. Within the basal part of the Flagstaff, specimens are limited to a single fossiliferous bed at each locality.

Remarks. This species is among the rarer ones found in the basal part of the Flagstaff formation, to which it appears to be confined in central Utah. Its failure to persist may be due to unfavorable conditions or to the competition of the ubiquitous *Hydrobia utahensis* White, with which it is invariably associated.

---

[3] This specimen is so thoroughly embedded in matrix that only its height could be measured.

The Flagstaff specimens appear to be identical with Meek's type in the U. S. National Museum (No. 2137). The Flagstaff specimens are excellently preserved, much better than those in the U. S. National Museum, and are numerous enough for positive identification.

Order PULMONATA
Suborder BASOMMATOPHORA
Family LYMNAEIDAE
Genus **Pleurolimnaea** Meek, 1866

Diagnosis. Shell dextral, small, thin, fragile, elongate-ovate, narrow; sutures well impressed; whorls higher than wide, moderately inflated, marked by distinct growth lines and regularly spaced axial costae parallel to but stronger than growth lines; aperture narrow, angular and unexpanded above, rounded and slightly flaring below; parietal margin of aperture reflected over umbilicus. *Type: Limnaea tenuicosta* Meek and Hayden, 1856.

Ecology. It would be hazardous to attempt to reconstruct the ecological preferences of *Pleurolimnaea* by analogy with living Lymnaeidae. The following data from collections from the lower part of the Flagstaff may be significant. *P. tenuicosta* was widespread in the Flagstaff lake but seldom abundant. In significantly large collections it forms no more than 14.6 per cent of total individuals and less than 10 per cent in most collections. The abundance of specimens collected nevertheless indicates that it was a fresh-water snail. On the other hand, it did not thrive in the Flagstaff lake environment, which evidently lacked some factor that was necessary to its well-being. In this respect, it differs from the smaller lymnaeids of the present day which live in large numbers in lakes presumably comparable to the Flagstaff lake or on wet muddy stretches along their margins. This may be another indication that it does not belong in the family Lymnaeidae.

Remarks. Baker (1911, p. 85, 91, 95) recognized the genus as valid, confirming Meek's (1876, p. 534) cautious suggestion that a new genus might be necessary for *Limnaea tenuicosta.* Yen (1948b, p. 43) has followed Baker. Anyone familiar with the range of variation in the pattern of ornamentation of the living Lymnaeidae would agree that *Pleurolimnaea* departs so radically from the usual limits that it cannot be placed under any of the existing genera even as a subgenus. The soft parts are unknown, so that even assignment to the family Lymnaeidae is a matter of convenience based on the assumption that the type species is a fresh-water species and that within the fresh-water groups it agrees best with the Lymnaeidae. Yen (1948b, p. 43) has summarized the situation as follows: "On morphological and on stratigraphical grounds, *Pleurolimnaea* Meek may be considered as a distinct genus, but its family assignment may need further consideration. The genus may belong to Ellobiidae and is possibly related to *Tortacella.*" There can be no doubt of the fresh-water nature of the species when the Flagstaff records are examined. No land snail could be found in such consistently large numbers with fresh-water associates in a lacustrine deposit.

Pleurolimnaea tenuicosta (Meek and Hayden), 1856
(Pl. 3, figs. 14–16)

Limnaea tenuicosta MEEK AND HAYDEN, 1856, Phila. Acad. Nat. Sci., Proc., vol. 8, p. 119
Limnaea (Pleurolimnaea) tenuicosta MEEK, 1876, Hayden Surv., Mon. 9, p. 534, Pl. 44, fig. 13
Pleurolimnaea tenuicosta BAKER, 1911, Lymnaeidae of N. and M. America, p. 85, 91, 95, Pl. 44, fig. 13
Lymnaea tenuicosta tenuicosta HENDERSON, 1935, Geol. Soc. Am., Spec. Paper 3, p. 241 (extensive bibliography)
Pleurolimnaea tenuicosta YEN, 1948, U. S. Geol. Surv., Prof. Paper 214–C, p. 43, Pl. 10, fig. 15

Diagnosis. Shell dextral, small, slender, thin, fragile; spire acute and elevated, slightly oblique; suture impressed; surface ornamented with fine lines of growth and sharply elevated, narrow axial costae, parallel to the growth lines.

Types. Hypotype, U. S. Nat. Mus., No. 560182 (Yen, 1948b, Pl. 10, fig. 15) ; hypotypes, O.S.U. Nos. 20045, 20947, 20948

	Height	Width	Ap. Height	Ap. Width	No. of Whorls
Hypotype, USNM 560182	13.1 mm	4.5	6	2.2	5
Hypotype, No. 20045	9	3	4	2	..
Hypotype, No. 20947	7.6	3.2	3.2	1.6	6
Hypotype, No. 20948	8.4	2.8	4	2	6

Occurrence. Lower part of Flagstaff formation, in 17 of 42 collections: coll. 10*, 3 specimens, *I*—8.3 per cent, *V*—1.9 per cent; coll. 13, 15 specimens, *I*—0.9 per cent, *V*—0.3 per cent; coll. 15*, 1 specimen; coll. 16, 58 specimens, *I*—4.0 per cent, *V*—7.9 per cent; coll. 17, 10 specimens, *I*—3.3 per cent, *V*—0.8 per cent; coll. 18, 2 specimens, *I*—0.9 per cent, *V*—6.1 per cent; coll. 19*, 1 specimen; coll. 20, 22 specimens, *I*—1.3 per cent, *V*—0.5 per cent; coll. 21*, 1 specimen; coll. 22*, 3 specimens; coll. 24, 5 specimens, *I*—0.4 per cent, *V*—2.7 per cent; coll. 25*, 4 specimens; coll. 27*, 37 specimens; coll. 34, 2 specimens, *I*—0.6 per cent, *V*—0.8 per cent; coll. 41, 42 specimens, *I*—7.1 per cent, *V*—33.2 per cent; coll. 47, 34 specimens, *I*—14.6 per cent, *V*—43.8 per cent.

Meek and Hayden's type is from the Fort Union "Eocene," near Fort Union, North Dakota. Henderson (1935, p. 242) has summarized the records from the literature, some of which he considers doubtful. Yen (1948b, p. 36, 43) records the species from the Paleocene part of the Fort Union in Montana.

Remarks. The Flagstaff specimens differ from the types (USNM 12488 and 560182) in being consistently smaller, more fusoid, and not as shouldered. They may be distinct enough to merit varietal rank.

The species is easily distinguished from all other gastropods in the Flagstaff by the pattern of ornamentation. Only *Goniobasis tenera* (Hall) has axial ornamentation of greater prominence combined with an acute spire, but it is easily distinguished from *P. tenuicosta* by the equally prominent spiral ornamentation, the different shape of the whorls, and the proportionally smaller aperture. The characteristic ornamentation of each of these species appears early in the development of the shell, so that even very young specimens can be distinguished with ease.

Family PLANORBIDAE
Genus **Gyraulus** J. de Charpentier, 1837

Diagnosis. Shell small, planispiral, ultradextral, with few, rapidly increasing whorls, fully exposed above and below, with a nearly median periphery, obtusely angulated, or carinated. Aperture oblique, lip simple, unexpanded. Ornamentation of fine, closely set axial striations in some cases crossed by fine spiral striations. *Type: Planorbis hispidus* Draparnaud

Ecology. The living members of the genus are found in shallow water with muddy bottom and prefer an environment with abundant vegetation. They are found in large numbers on water weed but tolerate a wide range of environmental conditions. They are ubiquitous in collections of fresh-water mollusks. In distribution, they are almost world-wide. The Flagstaff forms are relatively rare and do not occur in all collections. The Flagstaff habitat was one in which they could exist, but it did not offer optimum conditions. Their relatively small numbers do not appear to be the result of competition from other species but should rather be ascribed to the fact that the environment was less desirable than others; the environment which prevailed when the basal part of the Flagstaff formation was deposited was especially unfavorable to this group of snails.

Remarks. Two species are assigned to this genus with some doubt. The genus *Gyraulus* appears to be the most satisfactory assignment, but they both present characteristics which distinguish them from living and late Tertiary members of the genus.

Gyraulus militaris (White), 1880
(Pl. 3, figs. 17, 18)

Planorbis militaris WHITE, 1880, U. S. Nat. Mus., Proc., vol. 3, p. 159
Gyraulus militaris WHITE, 1880, Am. Jour. Sci., 3d ser., vol. 20, p. 46
Planorbis (Gyraulus) militaris WHITE, 1880, U. S. Geol. Surv., 3d Ann. Rept., p. 447, Pl. 28, fig. 10
Planorbis militaris HENDERSON, 1935, Geol. Soc. Am., Spec. Paper 3, p. 247
Gyraulus militaris YEN, 1946, Am. Jour. Sci., vol. 244, p. 45

Diagnosis. Shell small, dextral, planispiral, depressed above and umbilicate below; volutions, about 3; periphery abruptly to broadly rounded on upper and lower sides.

Types. Hypotypes, O.S.U. Nos. 20950, 20951

	Height	Width	Ap. Height	Ap. Width	No. of Whorls
Hypotype, No. 20950	1.2 mm	3	..	..	2
Hypotype, No. 20951	1	2.5	..	..	2.5

Occurrence. Lower part of Flagstaff, in 12 of 42 collections; upper part of Flagstaff, in 3 of 7 collections. It forms a small percentage of the collections in which it is found. It is never a conspicuous member of the fauna but is more abundant in the upper beds than in the lower ones. Collections from lower part of Flagstaff: coll. 13, 8 specimens, I— 0.9 per cent, V— 0.1 per cent; coll. 15*, 2 specimens; coll. 16, 28 specimens, I—2.0 per cent, V—0.7 per cent; coll. 17, 8 specimens, I—2.6 per cent, V— 0.9 per cent; coll. 18, 6 specimens, I—2.6 per cent, V—3.6 per cent; coll. 20, 32 specimens, I—1.8 per cent, V—0.7 per cent; coll. 22*, 1 specimen; coll. 24, 13 specimens, I—1.0 per cent, V—2.7 per cent; coll. 29, 2 specimens, I—0.8 per cent, V—0.1 per cent; coll. 34, 3 specimens, I—0.8 per cent, V—0.2 per cent; coll. 41, 18 specimens, I—3.0 per cent, V—2.8 per cent; coll. 46, 3 specimens, I—0.9 per cent, V—1.2 per cent; coll. 47, 1 specimen, I—0.4 per cent, V—0.3 per cent. Collections from upper part of Flagstaff: coll. 1, 75 specimens, I—23.3 per cent, V—0.7 per cent; coll. 29, 2 specimens, I—0.8 per cent, V—0.1 per cent; coll. 38, 5 specimens, I—8.5 per cent, V—0.1 per cent.

The species was originally described from "Laramie or Wasatch beds, head of Soldier's Fork, Utah", probably from beds now referred either to the upper part of the Flagstaff or the Colton.

Remarks. When well-preserved specimens are available, *Gyraulus militaris* is easily distinguished from *Gyraulus aequalis* by its smaller size for an equivalent number of whorls and the abrupt rounding or obtuse angulation of its whorls as compared with the even rounding of those of *G. aequalis*. Poorly preserved specimens are difficult to identify specifically.

Gyraulus aequalis (White), 1880
(Pl. 3, figs. 19–22)

Planorbis aequalis WHITE, 1880, U. S. Nat. Mus., Proc., vol. 3, p. 159
Planorbis aequalis HENDERSON, 1935, Geol. Soc. Am., Spec. Paper 3, p. 243

Diagnosis. Shell small, ultradextral; spire flat, suture impressed; whorls about 5, regularly increasing in size to the aperture. Surface marked by fine lines of growth.

Types. Hypotypes, O.S.U. Nos. 20057, 20952, 20953, 20954

	Height	Width	Ap. Height	Ap. Width	No. of Whorls
Hypotype, No. 20057	1 mm	2	0.7	0.6	2.5
Hypotype, No. 20952	1	4	0.8	0.7	2.5
Hypotype, No. 20953	..	6.3	..	..	4.5
Hypotype, No. 20954	..	7.6	..	..	4

Occurrence. Upper part of Flagstaff formation, in 2 of 7 collections; coll. 29, 13 specimens, I—5.5 per cent, V—0.2 per cent; coll. 38*, 2 specimens. The species was originally described from the Green River formation, Henry's Fork of Green River, Wyoming. Specimens agreeing with the type in most respects have been collected from the upper part of the Flagstaff, as has been noted.

Remarks. This species suggests a small *Planorbula* rather than a *Gyraulus* but it cannot be placed in that genus, for neither the types nor the Flagstaff specimens show any sign of internal lamellae. Its features agree most closely with those of *Gyraulus,* and it is accordingly referred to that genus here, although it may eventually prove to belong to a new genus, different from all the small planorbids at present known.

Genus **Carinulorbis** Yen, 1949

Carinorbis YEN, 1946, Am. Jour. Sci., vol. 244, p. 46, *non* Conrad, 1862
Carinulorbis Yen, 1949, Jour. Paleont., vol 23, p. 573
Diagnosis. "Shell of small size, nearly flat or slightly concave above and decidedly concave in the umbilical view. Whorls few, rapidly increasing in size, all visible on both sides; strongly carinated or keeled along the periphery and pronouncedly angulated at the latero-basal margin. The carina has a sharp and produced margin, which is not embraced by the succeeding whorl. Exposed surface of the whorls generally flat or gently concave, bearing fine but distinct lines of growth. Aperture slightly oblique and angular in outline. Umbilicus wide." (Yen, 1946, p. 46). *Type. C. planospiralis* Yen, 1946

Remarks. Yen's type species has a sharp carina and very flat-sided whorls which appear to be an extreme development of the generic characters. The species described hereafter is included in this genus because of its general agreement with the type species in all but the development of the carina. Yen (1946, p. 46) has compared his genus with *Platytaphius* Pilsbry and thinks it may be ancestral to *Angulorbis* Yen. To the student of living American planorbids, *Carinulorbis* suggests a miniature *Helisoma anceps* (Menke), but the resemblance is pure coincidence. Yen's species is from the Paleocene of Sheridan County, Wyoming; the Utah species adds considerably to the geographic distribution of the genus in the Paleocene.

Carinulorbis utahensis La Rocque, sp. nov.
(Pl. 3, figs. 23–26)

Description. Shell small, of about 4 whorls; spire sunken below body whorl; suture impressed; whorls narrow, regularly increasing in size to aperture, broadly convex on upper side; periphery rounded; umbilicus broad and deep; surface marked by fine, regular lines of growth.

Types. Holotype, O.S.U. No. 20955; paratype, O.S.U. No. 20956

	Height	Width	Ap. Height	Ap. Width	No. of Whorls
Holotype, No. 20955	1.3 mm	3	1.3	1	2.5
Paratype, No. 20956	1.3	2.3	1	1	2

Occurrence. Lower part of Flagstaff formation, at 5 of 42 localities: coll. 16, 5 specimens, I—0.4 per cent, V—0.2 per cent; coll. 17, 1 specimen, I—0.3 per cent, V—0.1 per cent; coll. 43, 1 specimen, I—1.9 per cent, V—0.2 per cent; coll. 46, 16 specimens, I—4.9 per cent, V—6.6 per cent; coll. 47, 4 specimens, I—1.7 per cent, V—1.0 per cent. It forms only an insignificant proportion of the molluscan assemblage in a given collection, never attaining more than 4.9 per cent of the total number of individuals and 6.6 per cent of the total volume.

Remarks. Carinulorbis utahensis La Rocque is distinguished from *C. planospiralis* by its more rounded whorls and less definite superior and inferior carinae. The agreement of other characteristics in the two species indicates that they are congeneric.

Family PHYSIDAE
Genus **Physa** Draparnaud, 1801

Diagnosis. Shell sinistral, oblong or elongated, thin, surface dull to shining, spire acute or depressed, usually shorter than aperture; columella with obscure plait or thickening, which gradually merges with callus of parietal wall; aperture narrowed above, rounded below; outer lip sharp, commonly thickened by a vertical callus; inner lip closely appressed to columellar region, usually closing umbilicus or, rarely, leaving a small chink or perforation;

sculpture of fine, closely crowded axial striae and coarse or subobsolete spiral impressed lines. *Type: Bulla fontinalis* Linn.

Ecology. Species of *Physa* are among the hardiest of fresh-water mollusks. They are found in all kinds of bodies of water, from temporary woodland pools to the largest lakes and rivers. The majority of them live in shallow water, from a few inches to several feet, but they have also been recorded from the bottom of deep lakes. Dawson (1911, p. 1–44) has summarized the ecology of the living species. Almost all kinds of fresh-water environments are acceptable to *Physa,* and in addition to the usual habitats described by Dawson (1911) species have been found living in sewage treatment plants, in moist patches of algae on vertical cliffs (Pilsbry, 1925, p. 325–328), and in hot springs at about 92° F. (Clench, 1926, p. 3).

Species of *Physa* are found in both the basal and upper parts of the Flagstaff formation but are absent from the middle part. Their absence in the lacustrine beds of the middle part of the formation is an indication of adverse conditions while these beds were being deposited. Judging from its present-day habitats, if the Flagstaff lake during mid-Flagstaff time had presented the least possibilities for the existence of mollusks, the first to invade would have been *Physa,* which was undoubtedly present not very far away, for it re-invaded the area as soon as the upper beds of the formation began to accumulate.

On the other hand, both in the lower and upper parts of the formation, *Physa* is not represented by great numbers of specimens. It forms but an inconspicuous element of the lower fauna and, although present in greater numbers and proportion in the upper fauna, it is not the dominant mollusk of that assemblage. This is one of the most puzzling features of the Flagstaff fauna, for in the Colton and Green River formations the genus is one of the dominant forms. The small numbers of *Physa* give the Flagstaff fauna a character of its own, which may be shared with other Paleocene and Eocene assemblages, although this suspicion cannot be confirmed until quantitative data are available for other Paleocene faunas.

Remarks. The genus is easily identifiable, even from fragmentary material, because of the sinistral spire of the shell. The only other genus with a sinistral shell in the Flagstaff fauna is *Albertanella;* the difference in size is sufficient to distinguish the two genera. Identification of species in *Physa* is more difficult as indeed it is for living species. Four species are recognized in the Flagstaff, and four collections can be identified only to genus either because they contain only immature individuals or because of the fragmentary nature of the material.

The relationships of the four species identified is interesting but far from clear. So far as present work indicates, *P. bridgerensis* is found in the basal Flagstaff, and even in the largest populations found there is no variation toward *P. pleromatis.* In populations of *P. pleromatis* from the upper part of the Flagstaff, there is a strong tendency toward *P. bridgerensis,* although there is seldom any doubt as to the identity of a particular specimen. The same tendency toward development of a high spire is evident in the Colton and Green River populations of *P. pleromatis,* but here the size of the specimens alone prevents any reference to *P. bridgerensis.*

The two smaller species of *Physa, P.* cf. *P. rhomboidea* and *P.* cf. *P. longiuscula,* have somewhat the same relationship as the larger two. *P.* cf. *P. rhomboidea* is an analogue of *P. pleromatis* and *P.* cf. *P. longiuscula* an analogue of *P. bridgerensis.* Both of these smaller species are found in the basal third of the Flagstaff and have not been found, up to the present, in the upper two-thirds of the formation. Two possibilities for the development of the upper Flagstaff and Colton-Green River populations of *Physa* may be considered. First, one may think of *P. pleromatis* as derived directly from *P. bridgerensis* during late Flagstaff time by the development of a more globose body whorl. This would be one interpretation of the populations of *Physa* in the upper part of the Flagstaff, where there is a strong tendency to the development of a narrow body whorl and a high spire. According to this hypothesis, the *P. bridgerensis* stock would be eliminated early in Colton time, and the species would continue into late Colton and Green River time as *P. pleromatis* (globose form), with a later development to very large size and a still more globose body whorl.

Secondly, one may think of *P.* cf. *P. rhomboidea* giving rise directly to *P. pleromatis* and *P.* cf. *P. longiuscula* to *P. bridgerensis.* In the second case (*longiuscula-bridgerensis*) the separation of the two stocks would have to be placed in the early Flagstaff, since *P. bridgerensis* is found in beds of that age. For the derivation of *P. pleromatis* from *P.* cf. *P. rhomboidea,* the matter is a little difficult. *P.* cf. *P. rhomboidea* has been found in the lower third of the Flagstaff of the Wasatch Plateau, but *P. pleromatis* is not found with it and is not developed fully below the upper third of the formation. The possibility still remains that the differentiation between *P.* cf. *P. rhomboidea* and *P. pleromatis* occurred elsewhere, but on present evidence the derivation of *P. pleromatis* directly from *P. bridgerensis* in the late Flagstaff of the Wasatch Plateau appears more likely.

Physa bridgerensis Meek, 1872
(Pl. 3, figs. 27–29)

Physa bridgerensis MEEK, 1872, Hayden Surv., 6th Ann. Rept., p. 516
Physa (Bulinus?) bridgerensis WHITE, 1883, U. S. Geol. Surv., 3d Ann. Rept., p. 450, 474, Pl. 30, figs. 9–10
Physa bridgerensis HENDERSON, 1935, Geol. Soc. Am., Spec. Paper 3, p. 258.

Diagnosis. Shell sinistral, large, subovate in outline; spire conical, of 5 regularly increasing whorls; length of spire and aperture about equal; surface marked by strong lines of growth.

Types. Hypotypes, O.S.U. Nos. 20064, 20092, 20906

	Height	Width	Ap. Height	Ap. Width	No. of Whorls
Hypotype, No. 20064	29 mm	14	17	10	6
Hypotype, No. 20092	..	11	..	..	5
Hypotype, No. 20906	23	15	17	7	5

Occurrence. Lower part of Flagstaff formation, in 4 of 12 collections: Flagstaff formation, subdivision doubtful, 1 collection, No. 52; coll. 5*, 1 specimen; coll. 37*, 5 specimens; coll. 42*, 26 specimens; coll. 43, 2 specimens, *I*—3.8 percent, *V*—6.9 per cent; coll 52*, 2 specimens.

Remarks. In the Flagstaff, the species can be distinguished from *P. pleromatis* and *P.* cf. *P. rhomboidea* by the more inflated shell of these two species; from *P. longiuscula* it can be distinguished by its larger size for an equivalent number of whorls.

Physa pleromatis White, 1876
(Pl. 3, figs. 30–32)

Physa pleromatis WHITE, 1876, Wheeler Surv. West of 100th Merid., vol 4, p. 211, Pl. 21, fig. 1; *Physa pleromatus* WHITE, 1880, Am. Jour. Sci., 3d ser., vol. 20, p. 46
Physa pleromatis HENDERSON, 1935, Geol. Soc. Am., Spec. Paper 3, p. 261

Diagnosis. Shell sinistral, large, ovoid; spire obtusely conical, of 5–6 whorls, the first 4 or 5 small and moderately inflated, body whorl greatly inflated; length of aperture more than twice that of spire; surface marked by very fine, closely spaced growth lines.

Types. Hypotypes, O.S.U. Nos. 20907, 20908, 20909

	Height	Width	Ap. Height	Ap. Width	No. of Whorls
Hypotype, No. 20907	33 mm	24	24	12	4
Hypotype, No. 20908	42	31	..	..	5
Hypotype, No. 20909	24	17	..	..	4.5

The proportions of this species are extremely variable; measurements of two forms which intergrade so completely that they are not worthy of formal recognition are given below.

(a) spire acute, body whorl expanding abruptly and strongly:

Height	Width	Ap. Height	Ap. Width
39 mm	19.5	24	11
34	24.0	27	16

(b) spire increasing regularly in size:

Height	Width	Ap. Height	Ap. Width
29 mm	18.5	21.0	16
27	16	18.5	9
32	16	21.5	13

The type measures: length 32, width 22 mm (Russell, 1931, p. 18). The hypotypes show extreme variants of these two forms.

Occurrence. Upper part of Flagstaff formation at 4 of 7 localities: coll. 1, 45 specimens, *I*—13.9 per cent, *V*—31.5 per cent; coll. 2*, 38 specimens; coll. 29, 65 specimens, *I*—27.4 per cent, *V*—55.6 per cent; coll. 38, 39 specimens.

Remarks. The shells show great variation and, even though this is known to be a common trait of this species, there may be at least two distinct strains in the Flagstaff populations. The variation is in the shape of the spire and the body whorl; one has an acute spire and abruptly expanding body whorl, the other has a more regularly increasing spire and body whorl. White (1876a, p. 211) has indicated that the two forms intergrade, and this is confirmed by the material from the Flagstaff formation.

Physa cf. P. longiuscula Meek and Hayden, 1856

(Pl. 3, figs. 33–35)

Physa longiuscula Meek and Hayden, 1856, Phila. Acad. Nat. Sci., Proc., vol. 8, p. 19, 278

Physa (Aplexus) longiuscula Meek and Hayden, 1860, Phila. Acad. Nat. Sci., Proc., vol. 12, p. 431

Bulinus longiusculus Meek, 1876, Hayden Survey, Mon. 9, p. 541, Pl. 43, fig. 16

Bulinus (Physa?) longiusculus White, 1883, U. S. Geol. Surv., 3d Ann. Rept., p. 451, 475

Aplexa? longiuscula Henderson, 1935, Geol. Soc. Am., Spec. Paper 3, p. 264

Diagnosis. Shell narrowly ovate, of about 5 whorls; spire high and pointed; whorls only slightly convex, regularly increasing; surface marked with fine, indistinct lines of growth; aperture narrowly subovate, acutely angular above and narrowly rounded below.

Types. U.S.N.M. Nos. 2120, 2121; Hypotypes, O.S.U. Nos. 20910, 20911, 20912

	Height	*Width*	*Ap. Height*	*Ap. Width*	*No. of Whorls*
Hypotype, No. 20910	20 mm	9	12	3.5	5
Hypotype, No. 20911	19	11	12	4	4.5
Hypotype, No. 20912	28	15	18	8	6

Occurrence. Lower part of Flagstaff formation, at one of 42 localities: coll. 53*, 6 specimens. The types are from "3 miles above Fort Union," *i.e.,* the Fort Union Eocene near Buford, North Dakota.

Remarks. The species is easily distinguished from *P. bridgerensis,* the only species with which it might be confused in Flagstaff collections, by its much smaller size and even more elongate outline. Our specimens correspond in size and proportions to Meek and Hayden's description and to their figures. The types of this species, identified by Meek and deposited in the U. S. National Museum (Nos. 2120 and 2121) have been examined. They are badly crushed and do not correspond with the figure of the species. It seems that Meek and Hayden gave the species rather wide limits and I am somewhat doubtful concerning the identity of the Flagstaff specimens with it. The species is placed in the genus *Physa* rather than in *Aplexa,* as was done by Henderson (1935, p. 264), who was tempted to place it in *Physa* on the basis of the figures. The species is rather more elongate than the usual living *Physa,* but it is not as elongate as typical *Aplexa.*

Physa cf. P. rhomboidea Meek and Hayden, 1856

(Pl. 3, figs. 36–38)

Physa rhomboidea Meek and Hayden, 1856, Phila. Acad. Nat. Sci., Proc., vol. 8, p. 119, 278

Bulinus? rhomboideus Meek, 1876, Hayden Surv., Mon. 9, p. 542, Pl. 43, fig. 17

Bulinus (Physa?) rhomboideus White, 1883, U. S. Geol. Surv., 3d Ann. Rept., p. 451, Pl. 25, fig. 9

Aplexa? rhomboidea Henderson, 1935, Geol. Soc. Am., Spec. Paper 3, p. 264

Diagnosis. Shell small, oval in outline, with short, pointed spire of about 5 whorls; aperture narrow.

Types. Hypotypes, O.S.U. Nos. 20913, 20914, 20915

	Height	Width	Ap. Height	Ap. Width	No. of Whorls
Hypotype, No. 20913	5.6 mm	3.6	3.3	2	4
Hypotype, No. 20914	4.3	2.6	2.6	1	3.3
Hypotype, No. 20915	5	3	3	1	3.5

Occurrence. Meek and Hayden's specimens came from the "Miocene 3 miles above Fort Union," *i.e.*, the Fort Union Eocene near Buford, North Dakota. It has been recorded from the Hell Creek beds of Montana and doubtfully from Wyoming. Lower part of Flagstaff formation, in 1 of 42 collections: coll. 9*, 4 specimens.

Remarks. Our specimens differ from the type only in being somewhat shorter and in having a slightly lower spire. They were at first confused with *P. pleromatis* White, which they resemble in proportions, but the dimensions for an equivalent number of whorls distinguished the two species. Our specimens can be referred to *P. rhomboidea* only with some doubt because of the differences which have been noted.

Physa, sp. undet.

Several lots of specimens undoubtedly referable to the genus *Physa* cannot be placed specifically because of poor preservation. They are added here for the sake of completeness. Lower part of Flagstaff formation, in 5 of 42 collections: coll. 9*, 5 specimens; coll. 10*, 2 specimens; coll. 13, 3 specimens, I—0.2 per cent, V—0.2 per cent; coll. 30*, 1 specimen; coll. 53*, 3 specimens. Upper part of Flagstaff formation, in 2 of 7 collections: coll. 1, 8 specimens, I—2.5 per cent, V—5.6 per cent; coll. 29, 2 specimens, I—0.8 per cent, V—0.4 per cent.

Family ANCYLIDAE
Genus Ferrissia Walker, 1903

Diagnosis. Shell limpetlike, ovate to oblong, conic, more or less elevated, apex eccentric and posterior, radially striate or smooth. *Type: Ancylus rivularis* Say

Ecology. The occurrence of species of *Ferrissia* and indeed of all the fresh-water limpets is governed by the habits and anatomy of the group. These are pulmonate (lung-breathing) snails, but they are able to draw oxygen from the water around them, for they are found in water too deep to permit the supposition that they must come to the surface to breathe at frequent intervals. The limpetlike shell affords protection to the soft parts of the animal, providing it can find surfaces to which it can cling. Fresh-water limpets are found clinging to stones, dead shells of other mollusks or fresh-water crustaceans, sticks and pieces of wood, and stems and leaves of aquatic plants, especially water lilies. The habit of clinging to various surfaces also aids in their dispersal. They have been found on the elytra of water beetles (Baker, 1928, p. 397), some of which fly long distances during the mating season, thus affording fresh-water limpets means of invading drainage systems which would otherwise be inaccessible to them. Occurrence of *Ferrissia* in the Flagstaff indicates that the several beds in which it is found afforded them a suitable environment; conditions were a little more favorable in the upper than in the lower part of the Flagstaff.

Occurrence. Species assigned to this genus have been recorded from the Paleocene and Eocene. The type species lives in streams of the eastern United States and Canada. At present, the genus *Ferrissia* has a world-wide distribution, with some important exceptions; it has not been found in Europe, Siberia, Syria, and the south shore of the Mediterranean, although it is recorded from the Nile Valley; there is a single, possibly introduced, species in Algeria. It is also absent from Mexico, Central America, and South America, but the absence may be more apparent than real and due to insufficient collecting, especially in Mexico and Central America.

Remarks. Generic identification in the fresh-water limpets presents some difficulties. Until about 1915 the classification of the group was in utter confusion. Bryant Walker brought order into this chaos and his classification of the living North American forms is summarized in his Synopsis (1918, p. 16 *et seq.*). His work was subsequently modified and expanded by the addition of a few genera and species, all based primarily on soft parts, especially the character of the radular teeth. Fossil species of fresh-water limpets had been recorded from the eighteen-sixties on, usually under the genus *Ancylus*. Attempts were made by Whiteaves (1885) and White (1886) to separate the fossil species from that European genus, but without notable success. Recently, Yen (1948b, p. 42) has created the genus *Palaeancylus* for a new species from the Paleocene of Montana and has referred some of the other species of *"Ancylus"* to *Ferrissia*. In practice, the shell characters of genera and subgenera established on soft parts must be used for the assignment of fossil species. In the case of the Flagstaff forms, the best that can be done is generic assignment to *Ferrissia* on the basis of the shape of the shell, its posterior, eccentric apex, and the absence of the dimplelike depression characteristic of *Palaeancylus*.

Ferrissia actinophora (White), 1886
(Pl. 4, figs. 1–2)

Acroloxus actinophorus WHITE, 1886, U. S. Geol. Surv., Bull. 34, p. 12, 26, Pl. 2, fig. 22
Ferrissia actinophora HENDERSON, 1935, Geol. Soc. Am., Spec. Paper 3, p. 266 (bibliography)

Diagnosis. "Shell small, elongate, subelliptical in marginal outline, somewhat wider in front than behind; apex situated at a little more than one-quarter of the full length of the shell from the posterior end. Surface marked by the ordinary lines of growth, which are crossed by a multitude of minute radiating lines, the latter being visible only under a lens." (White, 1886, p. 26, original description.)

Types. U. S. National Museum, No. 2136, 4 specimens; hypotypes, O.S.U. Nos. 20957, 20958

	Length	Width	Height
White's specimens	4 mm	3	?
Hypotype, No. 20957	4	2.6	1
Hypotype, No. 20958	2	2	1

Occurrence. Lower part of Flagstaff formation, in 1 of 42 collections: coll. 24, 1 specimen, *I*—0.1 per cent, *V*—0.1 per cent. Upper part of Flagstaff formation, in 2 of 7 collections: coll. 1, 30 specimens, *I*—9.3 per cent, *V*—0.3 per cent; coll. 29, 25 specimens, *I*—10.5 per cent, *V*—0.3 per cent. White originally recorded the species from "Wasatch strata near the town of Wales, Utah." Judging from the matrix in which one of the types is still partly enclosed, these specimens came from the upper part of the Flagstaff or Lower Colton of the Gunnison Plateau; they might also have come from the upper part of the Flagstaff or Lower Colton of the Wasatch Plateau. At any rate, they must be considered Eocene, if I am correct in my conclusions concerning the age of the divisions of the Flagstaff. It is one of the few species found in both the lower and upper parts of the Flagstaff.

Remarks. Although closely related to *F. minuta* (Meek and Hayden) this species appears to be distinct and entitled to specific rank. White. (1886, p. 26) stated that it was possibly identical with *F. minuta,* but pointed out that it had fine radial markings which that species did not possess. The Flagstaff specimens show no indication of radial ornamentation, but it is reasonably certain that they came from the same general area as the type locality and that some of them, at least, are from the same part of the Flagstaff formation. On the basis of location and after examination of White's type material in the U. S. National Museum, I have no hesitation in identifying the Flagstaff material with White's species. The fact remains that our specimens have no radial ornamentation, which may be due to poor preservation, and that White distinguished his species from *F. minuta* on the basis of that character. Yen (1948b, Pl. 10, fig. 14) has refigured *F. minuta,* and comparison of that figure with our specimens and White's figure shows that *F. actinophora* is consistently narrower than *F. minuta*. For the present I feel it is best to identify the Flagstaff material with White's species and to retain his name as valid.

Ferrissia ? sp. A

The single specimen collected is too poorly preserved to permit more than a doubtful assignment to the genus *Ferrissia*. It lacks the apex, whose characteristics cannot therefore be ascertained, but the arrangement of the growth lines indicates that it is subcentral. The growth lines are fine, regular, and strongly marked. The outline of the shell is subelliptical, the two ends of the shell almost equal. The shell substance is extremely thin. Lower part of Flagstaff formation, in 1 of 42 collections: coll. 23*, 1 specimen; length 2.5 mm, width 1.5 mm, height 0.5 mm.

Ferrissia ? sp. B

This species is also represented by a single specimen. The shell is high and narrow, irregularly conical, with a subcentral apex. Growth lines fine, crowded; outline of shell subelliptical, wider posteriorly. The shell substance is thin but somewhat thicker than that of *Ferrissia?* sp. A. Lower part of Flagstaff formation, in 1 of 42 collections: coll. 24, 1 specimen, I—0.1 per cent, V—0.1 per cent; length 2 mm, width 1.5 mm, height 1 mm.

Family CARYCHIIDAE
Genus Carychium Müller, 1774

Diagnosis. Shell small, dextral, elongate-cylindrical, spire blunt; whorls laterally flattened. Surface of whorl with inconspicuous axial ornamentation only. Lip reflected and thickened, with a single lamella on columella. *Type: C. minimum* Müller

Occurrence. At present, mainly holarctic, but extending southward to Java and Costa Rica. One Pleistocene and one Pliocene species.

Carychium cf. C. exile H. C. Lea, 1842
(Pl. 4, fig. 3)

Carychium exile H. C. LEA, 1842, Am. Jour. Sci., 1st ser., vol. 42, p. 109
Carychium exile PILSBRY, 1948, Land Moll. N. Am., vol. 2, pt. 2, p. 1058

Types. Hypotype, O.S.U. No. 20896
Occurrence. Lower part of Flagstaff formation, in 1 of 42 collections: coll. 20, 5 specimens, I—0.3 per cent, V—0.1 per cent.

Remarks. Five specimens from the basal part of the Flagstaff formation undoubtedly belong to the genus *Carychium,* although the reflected lip and the internal lamella are not apparent in any of them. The assignment of Paleocene specimens to a living species may seem anomalous, but the resemblance is so striking that the comparison seems justified. It is easy to argue that material so widely separated in time should be distinguished specifically, but the difference in age is not sufficient; it must be supported by actual differences in character; in this case, with the material on hand, none are apparent. Perhaps when more material is available distinctions can be made; at present, the comparison with *C. exile* is unavoidable, even if it suggests that the species may have lived from the Paleocene to the present.

Suborder STYLOMMATOPHORA
Family HELICIDAE (*sensu lato*)
Genus Helix Linnaeus, 1758 (*s. l.*)

Diagnosis. Shell globose or depressed-globose, imperforate or narrowly umbilicate; embryonic whorls smooth; typically 5-banded, but some or all bands may be absent. *Type: Helix pomatia* Linnaeus

Ecology. No detailed ecologic data need be given here since the relationship of the species listed with the genus *Helix* is highly problematical.

Occurrence. The genus as restricted by malacologists is represented by numerous species in Europe and Asia Minor. It is not indigenous to North America, and the only species on this continent are those which have been introduced here by man, the type species and *H. aspersa* Müller; they have established themselves in widely separated localities in the United States, Canada, and Mexico.

Remarks. The successors of Linnaeus assigned to his genus *Helix* hundreds of species which fitted in a general way the diagnosis given herein. The fragmentation of this mass of species into groups of generic rank has followed the recognition of constant and valid criteria in the soft parts of the animal which are accompanied by inconspicuous but equally constant characteristics in the shell. The North American species originally assigned to *Helix* have been placed in several different families, genera, and subgenera whose enumeration has no place here. Suffice it to say that these genera may also be characterized by minute differences in the shell and that there is no doubt of their distinctness from typical *Helix.* These facts, which are a commonplace of malacology, are emphasized here because of the peculiar situation of the fossil species assigned to *Helix.* It seemed perfectly logical, at the time when they were described, to place these fossil species in *Helix;* the problem at present is to find a more acceptable generic reference. Generic assignment has been achieved in some cases, but for the vast majority of fossil helicoid snails it has not. Henderson (1935, p. 132) has summarized the situation in this manner:

"If perfect material, with the soft anatomy, were available, probably most of the fossil species placed in this catch-all genus would be assigned to other genera, but it is useless to remove them from this genus only to assign them to other genera where their positions would be equally questionable."

Following this wise advice, I have retained the name *Helix* for the Flagstaff species, but I have attempted to show the uncertainty of the assignment by placing it in quotation marks.

"Helix" riparia White, 1876
(Pl. 4, figs. 4–9)

Helix riparia WHITE, 1876, Geol. Uinta Mts., p. 104, 130
Helix (Arianta) riparia WHITE, 1880, Am. Jour. Sci., 3d ser., vol. 20, p. 46; 1883, U. S. Geol. Surv., 3d Ann. Rept., p. 455, 475, Pl. 29, figs. 13–14
Helix? riparia HENDERSON, 1935, Geol. Soc. Am. Spec. Paper 3, p. 136 (extensive bibliography)

Diagnosis. Shell of medium size, subconical, with about 5 whorls; whorls slightly convex, suture moderately impressed; spire considerably produced, about half as long as entire shell; body whorl expanding rapidly and continuously; umbilicus small, closed by reflection of lip; aperture oblique, subovate in outline. Surface marked with fine, crowded growth lines.

Types. Hypotypes, O.S.U. Nos. 20916–20920

	Height	Width	Ap. Height	Ap. Width	No. of Whorls
Hypotype, No. 20916	16 mm	15	9	8	4.5
Hypotype, No. 20917	22	22	10	9	5
Hypotype, No. 20918	26	27	16	15	6
Hypotype, No. 20919	20	16	13	13	4.5
Hypotype, No. 20920	22	16	14	14	4.5

Occurrence. Entire Flagstaff formation. Lower part of Flagstaff, in 6 of 42 collections: coll. 4*, 5 specimens; coll. 9*, 4 specimens; coll. 42*, 1 specimen; coll. 48*, 5 specimens; coll. 50*, 7 specimens; coll. 53*, 18 specimens. Middle part of Flagstaff, one collection; coll 44*, 15 specimens. Upper part of Flagstaff, in 2 of 7 collections: coll. 2*, 2 specimens; coll. 40*, 10 specimens. Flagstaff formation, subdivision unknown: coll. 51*, 53 specimens. The species was originally described from the Upper Green River, Eocene, 8 miles below Green River Station, Wyoming.

Ecology. Although this species cannot be assigned with certainty to a genus, its characteristics indicate that it was certainly a land snail. Its presence in lacustrine deposits gives some indication of proximity of the shore line, either the shore line of the lake itself or that of islands within the lake. Its widespread distribution in the middle part of the Flagstaff of the Wasatch Plateau, together with the nature of the sediments in that part of the formation, indicates the striking change which must have taken place during the time represented in the environment of the lake. Where widespread lacustrine conditions had obtained, almost without interruption, in early Flagstaff time, there was now a body or a number of bodies of water unsuitable for the existence of fresh-water mollusks, into which small groups of land snails were washed from time to time. The haphazard distribution of the land snails, both laterally and vertically, indicates the presence of low islands in the basin of the Flagstaff lake, islands on which land snails could thrive for a time; they were wiped out either by rising of the lake level or the complete elimination of vegetation from the islands. Along the margins of the Flagstaff lake, *"Helix" riparia* and other land snails appear in large numbers, in red beds which are probably remnants of former soils, reworked by the lake's waters. Here *"Helix" riparia* is associated with other land snails, giving a glimpse of the rich population of land mollusks which existed in central Utah during Paleocene and Eocene times.

Remarks. It is relatively easy to establish identity between the Flagstaff specimens and White's, but the problem of a satisfactory generic assignment remains unsolved. The material available shows little of the external features of the shell; it reveals only that the shell substance was rather thick for a land snail, that the umbilicus was small in the early whorls and closed by the reflected lip in the adult shell, and that the ornamentation of the surface consisted of simple, fine growth lines of a character shared by several living and fossil genera. These characteristics are nevertheless sufficient to exclude this species from the genus *Helix s. s.,* for the latter has a transversely flattened body whorl, and the reflection of the lip is of a very different character. White (1880a; 1883) was aware of the difficulty and he placed his species in the subgenus *Arianta,* since elevated to generic rank and restricted to exclude the American species referred to the group. The American land snails which White had in mind are now placed in the genera *Helminthoglypta* and *Micrarionta,* which contain many species approximately similar in shell proportions with the Tertiary species. A few of these are: *Helminthoglypta berryi* Hanna (Pilsbry, 1939, p. 77); *H. californiensis* (Lea) (Pilsbry, 1939, p. 90); *H. arrosa mailliardi* Pilsbry (Pilsbry, 1939, p. 123); and *H. traski misiona* Chace (Pilsbry, 1939, p. 174), one of the few species with fine axial striation. The resemblance with some species of *Micrarionta* is even more striking, for example *M. kelletti* (Forbes) (Pilsbry, 1939, p. 215), especially the high-spired forms (Pilsbry, 1939, fig. 107, h, j, and k, p. 214)—*M. redimita* (W. G. Binney) (Pilsbry, 1939, p. 218); *M. tryoni* (Newcomb) and its subspecies (Pilsbry, 1939, p. 220); *M. intercisa* (W. G. Binney) (Pilsbry, 1939, p. 224)— except for the presence of distinct spiral striations. The resemblance between the Flagstaff shells and the modern ones is not sufficient to place the species in either *Helminthoglypta* or *Micrarionta,* for in most of these shells, and especially in the globose, imperforate, or narrowly umbilicate forms which it resembles most, the surface ornamentation consists of coarse axial ridges and malleations, both of which are absent in *"Helix" riparia.* On the basis of the characteristics of the fossil specimens, a good case could also be made out for assignment to *Cepolis* de Montfort, subgenus *Hemitrochus* Swainson, a group now living in Cuba, the Bahamas, and southern Florida with relatives in the lower Miocene (Tampa Silex beds) of Florida. (*See* Pilsbry, 1939, p. 29, for figures.) The danger of assignment to a living genus is demonstrated by these superficial resemblances. If *"Helix" riparia* were referred to *Helminthoglypta* it would be identified with a group now living from Lower California to Oregon, west of the Sierra Nevada; if to *Micrarionta* it would be listed with a group of similar distribution, but one that has penetrated farther east into Nevada (?), Arizona, and Sonora. The reference to *Cepolis* would lead to still more far-reaching suppositions concerning the migrations of that genus and its early Tertiary history, none of which would be founded on acceptable premises. In these circumstances, it seems best to leave *"Helix" riparia* without further generic assignment, with the understanding that *"Helix"* is here considered a form genus, without any implications except those of the broadest nature concerning the relationships of the Flagstaff form with living members of the genus.

Family CAMAENIDAE

Genus **Oreohelix** Pilsbry, 1904

Diagnosis. Shell dextral, discoidal to pyramidal, with 4–6 tubular or carinate whorls; periostracum thin or absent; embryonic whorls carinate, with radial striae or riblets and commonly some spiral sculpture; neanic stage with angular or carinate periphery. Aperture rounded or angular, toothless; peristome blunt and sharp; columellar margin not expanded or reflected. *Type: Helix strigosa* Gould

Ecology. The genus has been aptly named "Mountain Snail" for it is best developed in the mountain regions of North America; Pilsbry (1939, p. 415) has summarized its environmental preferences and has indicated the range of variation which it will tolerate. The species of the genus require calcium carbonate, and most of them are restricted to limestone outcrops and their vicinity. If their calcium carbonate requirements are satisfied, they will establish flourishing colonies in some of the most unlikely spots, for example on a bare, sun-baked summit at 8300 feet and the barren face of a limestone ledge (Pilsbry, 1939, p. 415). Their presence in fossil lacustrine assemblages indicates the presence of suitable conditions near the margins of the lake. That these conditions were not usual in the land area surrounding the Flagstaff lake is shown by the scarcity of *Oreohelix* in the Flagstaff formation.

Occurrence. In the living fauna, *Oreohelix* is found from southern Saskatchewan and British Columbia south to western Chihuahua, westward to Catalina Island, California, and eastward to the Black Hills of South Dakota and the loess of eastern Iowa. The fossil record has been summarized by Henderson (1935, p. 138) and Pilsbry (1939, p. 416). It ranges from the Upper Cretaceous to the present, although the Cretaceous species are somewhat doubtfully assigned, and the fossil record is lacking for the Oligocene and Pliocene.

Remarks. Assignment of fossil land snails to the genus *Oreohelix* is beset by the same pitfalls as those indicated for *Helix*. In this case, however, the characteristics of the shell afford firmer basis for assignment and none at all for reference to *Helix*.

Oreohelix sp.
(Pl. 4, fig. 10)

A single specimen, referable with some doubt to this genus, has been found in collection 52. Gilliland (1951, p. 31) records *"Helix" (Oreohelix?)* aff. *H. peripheria* White from the Flagstaff of the Valley Mountains without indication of its frequency.

Type: Hypotype, O.S.U. No. 20962

Family BULIMULIDAE
Genus Bulimulus Leach, 1814

Diagnosis. Shell oblong-conic; umbilicus narrow or closed; surface with axial growth lines only; aperture angulated above, rounded below, slightly expanded and thickened, columellar margin thin and reflected over umbilicus; whorls evenly rounded, regularly increasing in size, body whorl as long as or longer than spire. *Type: Bulimulus exilis* Gmelin

Ecology. This is a decidedly southern genus (from the standpoint of the present fauna of the United States) and one which has not penetrated very far, in the modern fauna, north of the southern boundary of the United States. At present, according to Pilsbry (1946, p. 6) the species of the United States fauna ". . . live upon bushes and other vegetation, upon which they aestivate, but they usually hibernate buried a few inches in the soil." During the summer they are dormant except during and immediately after rains.

Occurrence. In the living fauna, *Bulimulus* is widely distributed in South America, Central America, Mexico, and the southernmost United States. A closely related genus, *Hyperaulax*, placed by some under *Bulimulus* as a subgenus, is represented by a number of species in the lower Miocene of Florida. For details of the distribution of *Bulimulus* and *Hyperaulax*, see Pilsbry (1946, p. 2, 4). The Flagstaff record extends the range of the genus to the Paleocene, even if there is some doubt about the generic assignment of the specimens.

Remarks. The bulimulids found in the Flagstaff formation are referred to this genus rather than to *Hyperaulax* of the Miocene and *Drymaeus, Orthalicus,* and *Liguus* of the living fauna because their characteristics seem to agree more closely with *Bulimulus*. The reference to this genus is far from certain, as diagnostic characters, such as the sculpture of the embryonic whorls, are lacking.

Bulimulus ? sp.
(Pl. 4, figs. 11–14)

Description. Shell dextral, large for the genus, ovate-conic; whorls regularly increasing, neither swollen nor shouldered, body whorl as long as or longer than spire; umbilicus narrow, probably closed by reflection of aperture; aperture bluntly angulated above, rounded below; shell substance thin; surface ornamentation, lip, and apical ornamentation not preserved.

Types. Figured specimens, O.S.U. Nos. 20921–20924

	Height	Width	Ap. Height	Ap. Width	No. of Whorls
No. 20921	28 mm	14	14	7	5.5
No. 20922	27	17	16	9	5
No. 20923	28	16	13	9	5
No. 20924	30	15	13	7	6

Occurrence. Upper part of Flagstaff formation, in 2 of 9 collections: coll. 48*, 5 specimens; coll. 50*, 9 specimens.

Remarks. The specimens are so poorly preserved, lacking all external features, that it would be pointless to describe them as a new species. I have no doubt that if and when better material is available, the species will prove to be new, for the specimens figured differ from the earliest known *Bulimuli* (*Hyperaulax* of the Miocene) and are closer in general aspect to the group *Rhabdotus* Albers which has successfully invaded the United States in Pleistocene and earlier times and survived in the present fauna.

Pilsbry (1946, p. 2) has discussed the occurrence of fossil bulimulids in the United States and points out that the only living relative of the genus *Hyperaulax* is a species of Fernando Noronha Island, east of Brazil. The central Utah species represents an earlier invasion of bulimulids, probably from Mexico, and probably entirely independent of the later Floridian group. I have found no other record of bulimulids from the Eocene of North America and suspect that this may be due to confusion, natural enough because of poor preservation, of bulimulids with fresh-water genera such as *Viviparus* and *Campeloma*. In order to justify the reference of my material to *Bulimulus* and to avoid confusion with *Viviparus* in the future, the following differences between the two genera are emphasized. The shell in bulimulids is very thin as compared with that of the viviparids; this is one criterion which can be used even in poorly preserved material, for example internal molds where the space between the base of one whorl and the top of another is an indication of the thickness of the shell; in the material under consideration it can be recognized as extremely thin both in the small fragment preserved (Pl. 4, fig. 12) and from the nature of the sutures. The rate of increase of the whorls is another criterion useful in distinguishing the two groups; in the bulimulids the whorls increase rapidly in size, so that the last whorl is always longer than the spire; in the viviparids, the increase is more gradual. If the aperture is preserved, its characteristics will at once distinguish a bulimulid from a viviparid; the bulimulid has a thin callus deposit on the parietal wall, and that deposit is scarcely distinguishable from the shell material of the previous whorl; the opposite is true in the viviparids, in which the aperture is entire and the parietal border of the whorl continuous with the outer border. In fully adult shells, bulimulids can no longer be confused with viviparids, for the lip in adult bulimulids is reflected and thickened in a manner characteristic of some, but not all, land snails and never found in viviparids. In spite of the fact that the central Utah material is very imperfect, I am convinced of its bulimulid nature and hope that further collecting will yield material showing sufficient characteristics for description of this material as a new species.

Family UROCOPTIDAE
Genus Holospira von Martens, 1860

Diagnosis. "Shell of medium or small size, cylindric, terminating above in a conic spire, retaining all the whorls, rimate or perforate. Whorls 11–21 closely coiled, the first 1½ smooth, the rest either smoothish, striate or ribbed; the suture superficial; last whorl more or less built forward, rounded, without keel. Aperture small, obliquely pear-shaped, rounded or oval, the peristome expanded or reflected, continuous and usually free throughout. Internal column hollow, variously sculptured or smooth." (Pilsbry, 1946, p. 111.) *Type: Cylindrella pilocerei* Pfeiffer

Ecology. According to Pilsbry (1946, p. 111), all these snails live on limestone terrain, commonly in very hot and dry places.

Occurrence. This is a genus with numerous species, most of them on the Mexican plateau, with outposts as far as southern Arizona and central Texas to the north and southern Mexico to the south in the present fauna. Only two species have been recorded as fossils in the United States, *H. leidyi* (Meek) and *H. grangeri* Cockerell. The first was originally recorded from the base of the Bridger or top of the Green River group, 12 miles south of Fort Bridger, Wyoming, the other from the Torrejon Eocene, East Fork Torrejon Arroyo, New Mexico, and also near Nacimiento, New Mexico.

Remarks. The reference of the two fossil species to *Holospira* is in little doubt, although examination of the interior of the shell, to determine the character of the internal lamellae, will be necessary for assignment to a subgenus of *Holospira* or to a new genus, as pointed out by Pilsbry (1946, p. 113). The urocoptids, as represented by *H. leidyi,* ranged much farther north during Eocene time than they do at present. Although rare in the Flagstaff formation, together with *Bulimulus,* this species gives the Flagstaff fauna a southern, one might even say a Mexican, aspect.

Holospira cf. H. leidyi (Meek), 1872
(Pl. 4, figs. 15, 16)

Pupa? (Holospira?) leidyi MEEK, 1872, Hayden Surv., 6th Ann. Rept., p. 517
Holospira leidyi COCKERELL, 1906, Am. Mus. Nat. Hist., Bull., vol. 22, p. 459
Holospira leidyi HENDERSON, 1935, Geol. Soc. Am., Spec. Paper 3, p. 148

Diagnosis. Shell small, cylindrical, with bluntly conical spire; whorls more than 10 (no complete specimen is recorded), regularly but gradually increasing in size; surface ornamentation of slightly oblique axial striae; aperture unknown.

Occurrence. Flagstaff formation, at 3 localities: lower part of Flagstaff formation, coll. 37*, 3 specimens; Flagstaff formation, subdivision doubtful: coll. 49*, 1 specimen; coll. 51*, 1 specimen.

Meek's specimens came from the base of the Bridger or the top of the Green River group, 12 miles south of Fort Bridger, Wyoming.

Remarks. Even in fragmentary condition and poor preservation, specimens of this species can be recognized as members of the genus *Holospira.* Specific identification is another matter, for the two Eocene species, *H. leidyi* (Meek) and *H. grangeri* Cockerell appear to differ but slightly and may prove to be identical. I have therefore referred my specimens to *H. leidyi,* the senior species, with some doubt. The material is too fragmentary to yield significant measurements.

Family ENDODONTIDAE
Genus Discus Fitzinger, 1833

Diagnosis. Shell dextral, small, depressed to depressed-globose, opaque, openly umbilicate; rib striate, at least above periphery; whorls increasing very gradually; aperture toothless or having a columellar tubercle; peristome simple and thin. *Type: Helix ruderata* Studer

Ecology. The optimum environment of the genus is humid forest, under dead wood, and among rotting leaves and grass in rather wet situations. Some of the species are quite hardy and manage to exist in dry situations with little vegetation and poor cover. One of the commoner species of the living fauna, *D. cronkhitei* (Newcomb) has been collected at an elevation of 8000 feet in Colorado. The Rocky Mountain form, *D. shimeki cockerelli* Pilsbry occurs only at considerable elevations in groves of aspen or narrow-leaved cottonwood above 8000 feet.

Occurrence. Holarctic, widespread; the genus has been recognized in the American Miocene, Eocene, and Upper Cretaceous, and in the European Tertiary. Henderson (1935, p. 158) has summarized the fossil record under the genus *Gonyodiscus.*

Remarks. The range of variation in shell form within the genus is restricted. It ranges from low-spired to moderately globose, and the development of the axial riblets also varies from species to species. Nevertheless, these shells are well characterized by the combination of open umbilicus, presence of axial riblets, at least on the upper surface of the whorls, and the sharp, thin lip.

Discus cf. D. ralstonensis (Cockerell), 1914
(Pl. 4, figs. 17–19)

Pyramidula ralstonensis COCKERELL, 1914, Am. Mus. Nat. Hist., Bull. 33, p. 101, 325, Pl. 8, figs. 1–2.
Gonyodiscus ralstonensis HENDERSON, 1935, Geol. Soc. Am., Spec. Paper 3, p. 158
Discus ralstonensis PILSBRY, 1948, Land Moll. N. Am., vol. 2, pt. 2, 599

Diagnosis. Shell thin, discoidal; spire only slightly convex; umbilicus wide; whorls about 3, with fine axial striae appearing on the first whorl and becoming more pronounced on each succeeding whorl; last whorl deflected downward from the plane of horizontal coiling; aperture ovate.

Types. Hypotypes, O.S.U. Nos. 20959–20961

	Height	*Width*	*Ap. Height*	*Ap. Width*	*No. of Whorls*
Hypotype, No. 20959	2.3 mm	1.5	..	..	2.5
Hypotype, No. 20960	2	1.5	..	..	2
Hypotype, No. 20961	4	6	..	..	3.5

Occurrence. Flagstaff formation, at 4 localities. Lower part of Flagstaff, in 3 of 40 collections: coll. 27*, 1 specimen; coll. 28*, 63 specimens; coll. 53*, 1 specimen. Upper part of Flagstaff, in 1 of 9 collections; coll. 1, 23 specimens, I—7.1 per cent, V—0.3 per cent. The species was originally described from the Ralston beds, "probably of Wasatch formation," southeast of mouth of Pat O'Hara Creek, Big Horn Basin, Wyoming, but Russell (1931, p. 24) says they are "almost certainly" from Sand Coulee beds, in which he found the species as well as the Gray Bull Eocene. In the Flagstaff formation, the species is found in the basal and upper parts of the formation, in small numbers forming an inconspicuous part of the molluscan fauna.

Remarks. I have not seen the types, but judging from Russells' figure of the holotype (AMNH No. 22356), our specimens differ from it only in having a somewhat lower spire and slightly more rounded whorls. They are also consistently smaller than either the type or Russell's specimens, but this may be due to immaturity, as our largest specimen has only 3.5 whorls, whereas Russell's have 5. These inconsistencies between the types and the Flagstaff specimens do not permit certain identification with *D. ralstonensis.*

Family PUPILLIDAE
Genus Gastrocopta Wollaston, 1878

Diagnosis. Shell dextral, small, cylindrical, with a blunt spire and laterally flattened whorls; lip reflected and thickened, obstructed by a variable number of lamellae. Angular and parietal lamellae more or less completely united into one biramose, bifid, lobed or sinuous lamella (or rarely the angular lamella is wanting). Columellar lamella present; palatal folds present (except in *G. corticaria*). (Modified from Pilsbry, 1948, p. 871). *Type: G. acarus* (Bens.)

Occurrence. "Nearly world-wide in tropical and temperate regions, but wanting on many oceanic islands and in the recent European fauna, though represented there as Oligocene to Pliocene fossils." (Pilsbry, 1948, p. 871.)

Gastrocopta? sp.
(Pl. 4, fig. 20)

A single specimen from the basal part of the Flagstaff, collection 27*, 1 specimen, is undoubtedly a pupillid; it has the strongly reflected lip and the general aspect of the genus

Gastrocopta, including the nature of the external ornamentation. On the other hand, the lamellae, if they ever existed, cannot be seen because of the matrix obstructing the aperture. Very weak lamellae would not prevent assignment to *Gastrocopta,* as some species of that genus, for example *G. corticaria* (Say), have a weak dental armature. (*See,* for example, Pilsbry, 1948, p. 892, Figs. 1–4). The Flagstaff specimen resembles in a general way Russell's *Pupilla inermis* (Russell, 1931, p. 15), but it is too imperfect for identification with his species.

Type: Hypotype, O.S.U. No. 20052

Genus **Albertanella** Russell, 1931

Albertanella RUSSELL, 1931, Trans. Roy. Soc. Canada (3), vol. 25, sec. 4, p. 16

Diagnosis. "Shell very small, sinistral, elongate-ovoid, tapering. Aperture narrowly ovoid and apparently without teeth. No surface markings." (Russell, 1931, p. 16.) *Type: A. minuta* Russell 1931; upper beds of Saunders formation, probably Paleocene; west side of McLeod River, just below mouth of McPherson Creek, Alberta, Canada.

Albertanella minuta Russell, 1931
(Pl. 4, figs. 21, 22)

Albertanella minuta RUSSELL, 1931, Trans. Roy. Soc. Canada (3), Vol. 25, sec. 4, p. 16, Pl. 2, figs. 14, 15

Description. "Shell very small, sinistral, narrowly ovoid. Spire elongate and tapering, obtuse at apex; volutions four to five, slightly convex or faintly shouldered; suture impressed. Columella apparently imperforate. Aperture narrowly ovoid, abruptly rounded in front, acutely angulate behind, oblique to longitudinal axis of shell, apparently without teeth. No surface markings visible. Length of type, 1.8 mm.; width, 0.5 mm.; length of aperture, 0.6 mm."

Types. Hypotypes, O.S.U. Nos. 20963, 20964

	Height	Width	Ap. Height	Ap. Width	No. of Whorls
Hypotype, No. 20963	2.2 mm	0.6	0.5	0.3	5.5
Hypotype, No. 20964	1.8	0.6	0.5	0.3	5

Occurrence. Lower part of Flagstaff formation, in 1 of 40 collections: coll. 24, 6 specimens, *I*—0.4 per cent, *V*—0.3 per cent. The holotype is from the upper beds of the Saunders formation, probably Paleocene in age; west side of McLeod River, just below the mouth of McPherson Creek, Alberta, Canada.

Remarks. Our specimens agree in every respect with Russell's description and illustrations. In addition, some of them show suggestions of faint axial striae. These tiny snails may be mistaken at first for embryonic Physas, but the greater width and fewer whorls of the latter distinguish them. The species is probably not any rarer than other land snails in Paleocene deposits. It often escapes attention because of its small size and its resemblance to *Physa.* No ecological data are given, as the species is too rare in the Flagstaff collections to be informative on that subject.

REGISTER OF COLLECTIONS

(1) North wall of Fairview Canyon, T. 13 S., R. 5 E., Sanpete County, Utah. Upper part of Flagstaff formation, about 70 feet from the top; 1949; 322 specimens.

Species	No. Spec.	Per cent Indiv.	Per cent Volume
Elliptio mormonum La Rocque	12	3.7	9.5
Lampsilis spiekeri La Rocque	24	7.4	19.1
Sphaerium cf. *S. formosum* (Meek and Hayden)	38	11.9	3.6
Viviparus paludinaeformis (Hall)	17	5.3	11.9
Goniobasis tenera (Hall), form B	50	15.6	17.5
Gyraulus militaris (White)	75	23.3	0.7
Physa pleromatis White	45	13.9	31.5
Physa sp. undet	8	2.5	5.6
Ferrissia actinophora (White)	30	9.3	0.3
Discus cf. *D. ralstonensis* (Cockerell)	23	7.1	0.3

(2) Same locality as (1). Upper part of Flagstaff formation, near top; about 10 feet stratigraphically below preceding collection; 1949; 86 specimens.

Species	No. Spec.	Per cent Indiv.	Per cent Volume
Viviparus paludinaeformis (Hall)	46	53.5	51.3
Physa pleromatis White	38	44.2	42.4
"Helix" riparia White	2	2.3	6.3

(3) Same locality as (1). Lower part of Flagstaff formation, about 100 feet from base of formation; 1949; 12 specimens.

Elliptio mendax (White)	2	16.7	49.7
Viviparus trochiformis (Meek and Hayden)	7	58.3	50.1
Hydrobia utahensis White	3	25.0	0.2

(4) North wall of Canal Canyon, sec. 10, T. 16 S., R. 4 E., Sanpete County, Utah. Lower part of Flagstaff formation, 5 feet from base of formation. Collector J. R. Gill, 1948; 5 specimens, *"Helix" riparia* White.

(5) Same locality and collector as (4). Lower part of Flagstaff formation, float, 7 specimens.

Viviparus trochiformis (Meek and Hayden)	1	..	..
Lioplacodes tenuicarinata (Meek and Hayden)	5	..	..
Physa bridgerensis Meek	1	..	..

(6) Same locality and collector as (4). Upper part of Flagstaff formation, float. One specimen of *Physa pleromatis* not listed.

(7) The Horseshoe, a cirque on the Wasatch monocline, sec. 1, T. 17 S., R. 4 E., Sanpete County, Utah. (Nos. 6 to 10 are from the same measured section). Lower part of Flagstaff formation, 13 feet from the base. Collector J. R. Gill, 1948; 14 specimens.

Viviparus trochiformis (Meek and Hayden)	7	..	..
Lioplacodes mariana Yen	7	..	..

(8) Same locality and collector as (7). Lower part of Flagstaff formation, 40 feet from the base; 11 specimens.

Viviparus trochiformis (Meek and Hayden)	4	..	..
Lioplacodes mariana Yen	7	..	..

(9) Same locality and collector as (7). Lower part of Flagstaff formation, 47 feet from the base; 58 specimens.

Goniobasis tenera (Hall), form A	12	20.7	34.3
Hydrobia utahensis White	33	56.9	1.5
Physa cf P. rhomboidea Meek and Hayden	4	6.9	0.1
Physa sp. undet.	5	8.6	0.1
"Helix" riparia White	4	6.9	64.0

(10) Same locality and collector as (7). Lower part of Flagstaff formation, 151 feet from the base; 36 specimens.

Viviparus trochiformis (Meek and Hayden)	5	13.9	46.6
Goniobasis tenera (Hall), form A	10	27.8	46.6
Hydrobia utahensis White	15	41.7	1.1
Hydrobia cf. H. recta White	1	2.8	0.1
Pleurolimnaea tenuicosta (Meek and Hayden)	3	8.3	1.9
Physa sp. undet.	2	5.5	3.7

(11) Same locality and collector as (7). Lower part of Flagstaff formation, 196 feet above the base; 7 specimens, *Viviparus trochiformis* (Meek and Hayden).

(12) Same locality as (7). Lower part of Flagstaff formation, float. Collectors Essig, Reynolds, Bowman, Smyth, Crowl, and La Rocque, July 30, 1950; 127 specimens.

Species	No. Spec.	Per cent Indiv.	Per cent Volume
Elliptio mendax (White)	8	6.3	20.6
Viviparus trochiformis (Meek and Hayden)	103	81.1	76.2
Lioplacodes mariana Yen	10	7.9	2.0
L. tenuicarinata (Meek and Hayden)	6	4.7	1.2

(13) North wall of Pigeon Creek Canyon, sec. 31, T. 16 S., R. 4 E., Sanpete County, Utah. Lower Flagstaff tongue in North Horn formation, about 25 feet from the top of the tongue; 1950; 1526 specimens.

Species	No. Spec.	Per cent Indiv.	Per cent Volume
Elliptio mendax (White)	55	3.5	60.5
Sphaerium cf. *formosum* (Meek and Hayden)	4	0.3	0.2
Pisidium sp. undet.	2	0.1	0.1
Viviparus trochiformis (Meek and Hayden)	109	7.1	34.5
Lioplacodes mariana Yen	3	0.2	0.3
L. tenuicarinata (Meek and Hayden)	3	0.2	0.3
Hydrobia utahensis White	1315	86.0	3.4
Micropyrgus minutulus (Meek and Hayden)	9	0.6	0.1
Pleurolimnaea tenuicosta (Meek and Hayden)	15	0.9	0.3
Gyraulus militaris (White)	8	0.9	0.1
Physa sp. undet.	3	0.2	0.2

(14) Same locality as (13). Lower part of Flagstaff formation, float. Collectors Wambaugh, Kalman, and Smith, 1949; 2 specimens, *Elliptio mendax* White.

(15) North wall of Ephraim Canyon, NW¼ sec. 13, T. 17 S., R. 3 E., Sanpete County, Utah. Lower part of Flagstaff formation, 37 feet above the base. Collector J. R. Gill, 1949. Collections 15–24 are from a measured section of the Flagstaff formation 1075 feet thick from the top of the North Horn to the base of the Colton; (15)—45 specimens.

Species	No. Spec.	Per cent Indiv.	Per cent Volume
Hydrobia utahensis White	39	86.8	75.9
Micropyrgus minutulus (Meek and Hayden)	1	6.6	4.8
Pleurolimnaea tenuicosta (Meek and Hayden)	1	2.2	16.1
Gyraulus militaris (White)	2	4.4	3.2

(16) Same locality and collector as (15). Lower part of Flagstaff formation, 38 feet above the base; 1431 specimens.

Species	No. Spec.	Per cent Indiv.	Per cent Volume
Pisidium sp. undet.	4	0.3	0.5
Viviparus trochiformis (Meek and Hayden)	24	1.7	49.1
Lioplacodes mariana Yen	6	0.4	3.3
Goniobasis tenera (Hall), form A	17	1.2	17.3
Hydrobia utahensis White	1272	88.8	20.8
Micropyrgus minutulus (Meek and Hayden)	17	1.2	0.2
Pleurolimnaea tenuicosta (Meek and Hayden)	58	4.0	7.9
Gyraulus militaris (White)	28	2.0	0.7
Carinulorbis utahensis La Rocque	5	0.4	0.2

(17) Same locality and collector as (15). Lower part of Flagstaff formation, 40 feet above the base; 300 specimens.

Species	No. Spec.	Per cent Indiv.	Per cent Volume
Elliptio mendax (White)	2	0.7	68.6
Lioplacodes tenuicarinata (Meek and Hayden)	3	1.0	7.9
Hydrobia utahensis White	272	90.8	21.4
Micropyrgus minutulus (Meek and Hayden)	4	1.3	0.3
Pleurolimnaea tenuicosta (Meek and Hayden)	10	3.3	0.8
Gyraulus militaris (White)	8	2.6	0.9
Carinulorbis utahensis La Rocque	1	0.3	0.1

(18) Same locality and collector as (15). Lower part of Flagstaff formation, 42 feet above the base; 228 specimens.

Species	No. Spec.	Per cent Indiv.	Per cent Volume
Pisidium sp. undet.	4	1.8	12.1
Hydrobia utahensis White	208	91.1	75.8
Micropyrgus minutulus (Meek and Hayden)	8	3.5	2.4
Pleurolimnaea tenuicosta (Meek and Hayden)	2	0.9	6.1
Gyraulus militaris (White)	6	2.6	3.6

(19) Same locality and collector as (15). Lower part of Flagstaff formation, 56 feet above the base; 34 specimens.

Species	No. Spec.	Per cent Indiv.	Per cent Volume
Pisidium sp. undet.	1	2.9	17.3
Hydrobia utahensis White	31	91.3	63.7
Micropyrgus minutulus (Meek and Hayden)	1	2.9	1.7
Pleurolimnaea tenuicosta (Meek and Hayden)	1	2.9	17.3

(20) Same locality and collector as (15). Lower part of Flagstaff formation, 60 feet above the base; 1769 specimens.

Species	No. Spec.	Per cent Indiv.	Per cent Volume
Elliptio mendax (White)	12	0.7	1.3
Sphaerium cf. S. formosum (Meek and Hayden)	7	0.4	0.3
Pisidium sp. undet.	45	2.5	1.0
Viviparus trochiformis (Meek and Hayden)	66	3.7	23.6
Lioplacodes limnaeiformis (Meek and Hayden)	10	0.6	0.9
L. mariana Yen	456	25.7	38.5
L. tenuicarinata (Meek and Hayden)	199	11.3	17.0
Goniobasis tenera (Hall), form A	23	1.3	3.6
G. tenera (Hall), form D	64	3.6	10.3
Hydrobia utahensis White	566	32.0	1.5
Micropyrgus minutulus (Meek and Hayden)	262	14.8	0.7
Pleurolimnaea tenuicosta (Meek and Hayden)	22	1.3	0.5
Gyraulus militaris (White)	32	1.8	0.7
Carychium cf. C. exile H. C. Lea	5	0.3	0.1

(21) Same locality and collector as (15). Lower part of Flagstaff formation, 73 feet above the base; 68 specimens.

Species	No. Spec.	Per cent Indiv.	Per cent Volume
Pisidium sp. undet.	8	11.8	12.2
Viviparus trochiformis (Meek and Hayden)	1	1.4	22.7
Lioplacodes mariana Yen	6	8.8	36.4
L. tenuicarinata (Meek and Hayden)	3	4.4	18.2
Hydrobia utahensis White	44	64.9	8.2
Micropyrgus minutulus (Meek and Hayden)	5	7.3	0.8
Pleurolimnaea tenuicosta (Meek and Hayden)	1	1.4	1.5

(22) Same locality and collector as (15). Lower part of Flagstaff formation, 141 feet above the base; 26 specimens.

Species	No. Spec.	Per cent Indiv.	Per cent Volume
Viviparus trochiformis (Meek and Hayden)	1	3.8	72.5
Hydrobia utahensis White	21	80.8	12.1
Pleurolimnaea tenuicosta (Meek and Hayden)	3	11.6	14.4
Gyraulus militaris (White)	1	3.8	1.0

(23) Same locality and collector as (15). Lower part of Flagstaff formation, 152 feet above the base; 4 specimens.

Species	No. Spec.	Per cent Indiv.	Per cent Volume
Pisidium sp. undet.	1	25.0	..
Hydrobia utahensis White	2	50.0	..
Ferrissia sp. A	1	25.0	..

(24) Same locality and collector as (15). Lower part of Flagstaff formation, 165 feet above the base; 1328 specimens.

Species	No. Spec.	Per cent Indiv.	Per cent Volume
Pisidium sp. undet.	1	0.1	0.6
Lioplacodes tenuicarinata (Meek and Hayden)	4	0.3	8.7
Hydrobia utahensis White	1297	97.6	84.8
Pleurolimnaea tenuicosta (Meek and Hayden)	5	0.4	2.7
Gyraulus militaris (White)	13	1.0	2.7
Ferrissia actinophora (White)	1	0.1	0.1
Ferrissia sp. B	1	0.1	0.1
Albertanella minuta Russell	6	0.4	0.3

(25) North wall of Ephraim Canyon, NW ¼ sec. 13, T. 17 S., R. 3 E., Sanpete County, Utah. Lower part of Flagstaff formation, 34 feet above the base; collector J. R. Gill, 1948; 23 specimens; (25) to (28) are from a section measured a few hundred feet east of the section represented by (15) to (24).

Species	No. Spec.	Per cent Indiv.	Per cent Volume
Viviparus trochiformis (Meek and Hayden)	4	17.4	..
Hydrobia utahensis White	15	65.2	..
Pleurolimnaea tenuicosta (Meek and Hayden)	4	17.4	..

(26) Same locality and collector as (25). Lower part of Flagstaff formation, 36 feet above the base; 103 specimens, *Hydrobia utahensis* White.

(27) Same locality and collector as (25). Lower part of Flagstaff formation, 52 feet above the base; 39 specimens.

Pleurolimnaea tenuicosta (Meek and Hayden)	37	94.8	..
Discus cf. *D. ralstonensis* (Cockerell)	1	2.6	..
Gastrocopta? sp.	1	2.6	..

(28) Same locality and collector as (25). Lower part of Flagstaff formation, 54 feet above the base; 67 specimens.

Sphaerium cf. *S. formosum* (Meek and Hayden)	4	5.9	..
Discus cf. *D. ralstonensis* (Cockerell)	63	94.1	..

(29) North wall of Ephraim Canyon, NW ¼ sec. 13, T. 17 S., R. 3 E., Sanpete County, Utah. Upper part of Flagstaff formation, 818 feet above the base of the formation; 237 specimens. Collectors J. R. Gill and A. La Rocque. This collection is from the same section as (15) to (24).

Elliptio mormonum La Rocque	3	1.3	2.8
Sphaerium cf. *S. formosum* (Meek and Hayden)	4	1.7	0.5
Viviparus paludinaeformis (Hall)	10	4.2	8.6
Goniobasis tenera (Hall), form B	73	30.9	31.2
Hydrobia ephraimensis La Rocque	40	16.9	0.3
Gyraulus militaris (White)	2	0.8	0.1
G. aequalis (White)	13	5.5	0.2
Physa pleromatis White	65	27.4	55.6
Physa sp. undet.	2	0.8	0.4
Ferrissia actinophora (White)	25	10.5	0.3

(30) North wall of Willow Creek, T. 17 S., R. 4 E., Sanpete County, Utah. Lower part of Flagstaff formation, 54 feet above the base; 1950; 30 specimens.

Viviparus trochiformis (Meek and Hayden)	4	13.3	47.0
Lioplacodes mariana Yen	14	46.7	43.8
Goniobasis tenera (Hall), form A	1	3.3	5.9
Hydrobia utahensis White	10	33.4	1.0
Physa sp. undet.	1	3.3	2.3

(31) Same locality as (30). Lower part of Flagstaff formation, 343 feet above the base. Collector J. R. Gill, 1948; 37 specimens.

Viviparus trochiformis (Meek and Hayden)	3	8.1	28.2
Goniobasis tenera (Hall), form A	15	40.6	80.3
Hydrobia utahensis White	16	43.2	1.2
Hydrobia cf. *H. recta* White	3	8.1	0.3

(32) East scarp of the shoulder graben, at the head of Willow Creek, T. 17 S., R. 4 E., Sanpete County, Utah. Lower part of Flagstaff formation, about 300 feet above the base. Collector J. R. Gill, 1948; 2 specimens, *Viviparus trochiformis* (Meek and Hayden).

(33) North wall of Manti Canyon, sec. 9, T. 18 S., R. 2 E., Sanpete County, Utah. Lower part of Flagstaff formation, 80 feet above the base. Collectors J. R. Gill and A. La Rocque, 1949; 55 specimens.

Species	No. Spec.	Per cent Indiv.	Per cent Volume
Elliptio mendax (White)	2	3.6	..
Viviparus trochiformis (Meek and Hayden)	12	21.8	..
Hydrobia utahensis White	41	74.6	..

(34) Same locality and collectors as (33). Lower part of Flagstaff formation, 83 feet above the base; 354 specimens.

Species	No. Spec.	Per cent Indiv.	Per cent Volume
Viviparus trochiformis (Meek and Hayden)	3	0.9	19.1
Lioplacodes mariana Yen	32	9.0	54.2
L. tenuicarinata (Meek and Hayden)	4	1.2	6.8
Goniobasis tenera (Hall), form A	1	0.3	3.2
Hydrobia utahensis White	291	82.2	14.8
H. cf. *H. recta* White	18	5.0	0.9
Pleurolimnaea tenuicosta (Meek and Hayden)	2	0.6	0.8
Gyraulus militaris (White)	3	0.8	0.2

(35) Same locality and collectors as (33). Lower part of Flagstaff formation, float from (33) and (34); 174 specimens.

Species	No. Spec.	Per cent Indiv.	Per cent Volume
Elliptio mendax (White)	1	0.6	7.2
Viviparus trochiformis (Meek and Hayden)	12	6.9	25.0
Lioplacodes mariana Yen	98	56.3	54.3
L. tenuicarinata (Meek and Hayden)	23	13.2'	12.8
Hydrobia utahensis White	40	23.0	0.7

(36) Same locality and collectors as (33). Lower part of Flagstaff formation, float; 58 specimens.

Species	No. Spec.	Per cent Indiv.	Per cent Volume
Elliptio mendax (White)	5	8.6	72.2
Viviparus trochiformis (Meek and Hayden)	4	6.9	16.6
Lioplacodes tenuicarinata (Meek and Hayden)	9	15.6	9.9
Hydrobia utahensis White	40	68.9	1.3

(37) Same locality and collectors as (33). Lower part of Flagstaff formation, 130 feet above the base; 8 specimens.

Species	No. Spec.	Per cent Indiv.	Per cent Volume
Physa bridgerensis Meek	5	..	..
Holospira cf. *H. leidyi* (Meek)	3	..	..

(38) Same locality and collectors as (33). Upper part of Flagstaff formation, 402 feet above the base; 59 specimens.

Species	No. Spec.	Per cent Indiv.	Per cent Volume
Viviparus paludinaeformis (Hall)	6	10.2	12.4
Goniobasis tenera (Hall), form B	7	11.8	7.2
Gyraulus militaris (White)	5	8.5	0.1
Gyraulus aequalis (White)	2	3.4	0.1
Physa pleromatis White	39	66.1	80.2

(39) East scarp of the shoulder graben, head of Manti Canyon, sec. 19, T. 18 S., R. 4 E., Sanpete County, Utah. Lower part of Flagstaff formation, 107 feet above the base. Collector J. R. Gill, 1948; 74 specimens, *Micropyrgus minutulus* (Meek and Hayden).

(40) Sixmile Canyon, near the head of Funk's Cove, T. 18 S., R. 3 E., Sanpete County, Utah. Upper part of Flagstaff formation, exact stratigraphic position not known. Collectors Grafton and Sanders, 1947; 120 specimens.

Species	No. Spec.	Per cent Indiv.	Per cent Volume
Viviparus paludinaeformis (Hall)	27	22.5	27.9
Goniobasis tenera (Hall), form B	83	69.2	43.1
"*Helix*" *riparia* White	10	8.3	29.0

(41) South slope of Wagon Road Ridge, T. 17 S., R. 5 E., Sanpete County Utah. Lower part of Flagstaff formation, about 100 feet above the base; 1950; 596 specimens.

Species	No. Spec.	Per cent Indiv.	Per cent Volume
Sphaerium cf. *S. formosum* (Meek and Hayden)	1	0.2	1.6
Viviparus trochiformis (Meek and Hayden)	1	0.2	11.8
Hydrobia utahensis White	532	89.1	50.4
Micropyrgus minutulus (Meek and Hayden)	2	0.4	0.2
Pleurolimnaea tenuicosta (Meek and Hayden)	42	7.1	33.2
Gyraulus militaris (White)	18	3.0	2.8

(42) North wall of Twelvemile Canyon, T. 19 S., R. 2 E., Sanpete County, Utah. Lower Flagstaff tongue in North Horn formation; 70 feet above the base of the tongue; 1949; 68 specimens.

Viviparus trochiformis (Meek and Hayden)	13	19.1	29.8
Lioplacodes limnaeiformis (Meek and Hayden)	1	1.5	0.6
L. tenuicarinata (Meek and Hayden)	5	7.3	3.0
Hydrobia utahensis White	22	32.4	0.4
Physa bridgerensis Meek	26	38.2	59.8
"*Helix*" *riparia* White	1	1.5	6.4

(43) Same locality and collector as (42). Lower Flagstaff tongue in North Horn formation; 75 feet above the base of the tongue; 53 specimens.

Viviparus trochiformis (Meek and Hayden)	5	9.4	86.7
Hydrobia utahensis White	45	84.9	6.2
Carinulorbis utahensis La Rocque	1	1.9	0.2
Physa bridgerensis Meek	2	3.8	6.9

(44) Same locality and collector as (42). Middle part of Flagstaff formation, about 625 feet above the base of the formation; 15 specimens, all "*Helix*" *riparia* White.

(45) Same locality as (42). Upper part of Flagstaff formation, 25 feet from the top of the formation. Collector G. K. Ealy, 1950; 330 specimens.

Viviparus paludinaeformis (Hall)	250	75.8	..
Goniobasis tenera (Hall), form B	80	24.2	..

(46) East slope of Musinia Peak, head of Willow Creek (south), T. 20 S., R. 2 E., Sanpete County, Utah. Lower part of Flagstaff formation, about 45 feet above the base; 1950; 325 specimens.

Lioplacodes mariana Yen	1	0.3	8.2
Hydrobia utahensis White	284	87.4	70.4
Micropyrgus minutulus (Meek and Hayden)	16	4.9	3.3
Pleurolimnaea tenuicosta (Meek and Hayden)	5	1.6	10.3
Gyraulus militaris (White)	3	0.9	1.2
Carinulorbis utahensis La Rocque	16	4.9	6.6

(47) Same locality and collector as (46). Lower part of Flagstaff formation, about 60 feet above the base; 233 specimens.

Lioplacodes tenuicarinata (Meek and Hayden)	5	2.1	25.7
Hydrobia utahensis White	189	81.2	29.2
Pleurolimnaea tenuicosta (Meek and Hayden)	34	14.6	43.8
Gyraulus militaris (White)	1	0.4	0.3
Carinulorbis utahensis La Rocque	4	1.7	1.0

(48) Little Salt Creek, Gunnison Plateau, Juab County, Utah, long. 111° 45′, lat. 39° 50′, approximately. Middle or upper part of Flagstaff formation, near base; probably upper Flagstaff. Collector R. E. Hunt, 1950; 10 specimens.

"*Helix*" *riparia* White	5	..	..
Bulimulus? sp.	5	..	..

(49) Mouth of Buck Hollow, Gunnison Plateau, Sanpete County, Utah. Flagstaff formation, exact stratigraphic position not known, but probably middle or upper part of Flagstaff. Collector C. H. Summerson, 1949; 1 specimen, *Holospira* cf. *H. leidyi* (Meek).

(50) North of Bear Canyon, Gunnison Plateau, Juab County, Utah. Flagstaff formation, 21 feet above the base; middle or upper part of Flagstaff formation. Collector R. E. Hunt, 1950; 16 specimens.

Species	No. Spec.	Per cent Indiv.	Per cent Volume
"Helix" riparia White	7	..	..
Bulimulus? sp.	9	..	..

(51) Just south of road into Spring Valley, Long Ridge, Juab County, Utah, long. 111° 55′, lat. 39° 40′, approximately. Middle or upper part of Flagstaff formation, isolated outcrop surrounded by North Horn conglomerate. Collector S. J. Muessig, 1949; 54 specimens.

"Helix" riparia White	53	..	..
Holospira cf. *H. leidyi* (Meek)	1	..	..

(52) About 1 mile north of Mills Gap, Long Ridge, Juab County, Utah, long. 111° 59′, lat. 39° 35′, approximately. Flagstaff formation, 130 feet above base; probably from upper part of Flagstaff. Collector S. J. Muessig, 1949; 3 specimens.

Physa bridgerensis Meek	2	..	..
Oreohelix sp.	1	..	..

(53) Round Valley, Valley Mountains. Lower part of Flagstaff formation, exact stratigraphic position unknown. Collector H. K. Lautenschlager, 1951; 40 specimens.

Viviparus trochiformis (Meek and Hayden)	12	30.0	18.0
Physa cf. *P. longiuscula* Meek and Hayden	6	15.0	1.9
Physa sp. undet.	3	7.5	0.9
"Helix" riparia White	18	45.0	78.5
Discus cf. *D. ralstonensis* (Cockerell)	1	2.5	0.1

(54) Mouth of Manti Canyon, T. 18 S., R. 2 E., Sanpete County, Utah. Colton formation, probably near the base. Collector K. E. Boker, 1952; 50 specimens, all *Goniobasis tenera* (Hall), form C.

PALEOECOLOGY

GENERAL

A modern lake may be described according to the nature of its bed, the chemical composition of its water, its fauna, the general climatic setting, and the seasonal variation observable in these factors. For an extinct lake, some of these factors may be deduced from the nature of the sediments, their lateral and vertical variation, their source, and the nature of the fauna preserved. Other factors are too evanescent to influence, except very imperfectly, either the sediments or the fauna. On the other hand, the sediments and the fauna together reveal something of the change of conditions within the lake from its inception to its extinction. This aspect of lake development is not easily available to the ecologist except in a lake whose size has diminished with time. To the paleoecologist, it is one of the most easily available fields of investigation and one which yields some of his most interesting results. The Flagstaff lake is an outstanding example of variations in sediments and faunas. Three phases of development are recognized. This account of the paleoecology of the lake is therefore divided into three parts.

EARLY FLAGSTAFF ENVIRONMENT

SIZE OF THE LAKE: In its first phase, the Flagstaff lake occupied an area in what is now the Wasatch Plateau; this area was much smaller than that which it occupied later. Possibly its supposed southern extension in the Valley Mountains and the Pavant Range was a separate lake for a while. During early Flagstaff time the area of the lake was large (Fig. 2), about the size of present-day Great Salt Lake. Large lakes develop in one way and smaller lakes, which are commonly no more than temporary widenings of a river system develop in another way. One of the main differences between large and small lakes is the variety of depositional environments in the former and the narrow range in the latter. Large lakes are commonly quite deep and are more likely to have steep shores; the early Flagstaff lake was an exception to this general rule; all evidence points to a shallow lake with low shore lines. For comparisons with modern lakes one must turn to large shallow lakes, such as Lake Erie, rather than to deeper bodies of water such as the other Great Lakes. Several factors in the paleoecological situation of large shallow lakes are affected by the size of the lake. For example, such lakes usually have a central area which, although shallow, receives finer sediments than the margins of the lake in which the coarser clastic sediments settle. Other factors peculiar to large shallow lakes are discussed at length in treatises on limnology and need not be emphasized here.

DEPTH OF WATER: Four factors indicate that the early Flagstaff lake was generally shallow: (1) the common occurrence of ripple marks on many beds; (2) the abundance of Mollusca, confined by their food requirements to shallow water; (3) the evidence of wave action, revealed by the high proportion of shell fragments in many beds; and (4) the abrupt lateral and vertical variation of the beds, unlikely in a deep-water environment. Conditions varied throughout the duration of the early Flagstaff lake, for the nature of the sediments also suggests that relatively deep areas existed from time to time and from place to place where Mollusca did not thrive, possibly because the water was too deep, and where almost pure limestones were being deposited. Even in these relatively pure limestones, fragments of shells were washed in, indicating that shallow-water conditions existed not far away.

CHEMICAL COMPOSITION OF THE WATER: The early Flagstaff lake was undoubtedly a "hard-water" lake, for the overwhelming majority of its beds contain a high proportion of calcium carbonate. Calcium carbonate brought to the lake in solution, was being deposited continuously; therefore, at any given time, the calcium carbonate content of the water was high, possibly as high as that of the marl lakes of the present day in which calcium carbonate is constantly deposited and replenished. Other dissolved chemicals may have been present, but if so they were not abundant enough to leave more than traces of their presence. The sedimentary environment at this time was certainly unfavorable to the accumulation of silica, for the part of the Flagstaff formation deposited at this time is remarkably free of chert.

FLUCTUATIONS OF THE SHORE LINE: In at least two places, Pigeon Hollow and Twelvemile Canyon, the lower part of the Flagstaff is invaded by tongues of the North Horn formation. These indicate temporary restrictions of the lake area by the influx of alluvial-plain sediments similar to those of the North Horn formation which, in the normal sequence, underlies the Flagstaff. Alluvial-plain deposition continued around the margins of the Flagstaff lake, and sometimes, perhaps in response to the stimulus of local orogenic movements, it encroached upon the area of the lake. These encroachments are relatively minor compared with the total area of the lake, but they must be taken into account.

SURROUNDING LAND SURFACE: Some account of the land area surrounding the Flagstaff lake must be given, as it is from this area that the sediments of the lake and the dissolved chemicals of its waters were derived. The early Flagstaff lake was probably surrounded by an area of low relief, for coarse clastic rocks are rare in the lower part of the section, and numerous beds of limestone indicate temporary cessations of the influx of clastic materials. This statement must be qualified, for the pre-Flagstaff sediments were mostly unconsolidated muds and sands which could be swept into the lake from a surface of considerable relief without producing deposits of coarse clastic rocks. If such relief did exist, it was soon considerably reduced. In the second phase of the lake, during which it enlarged, the Flagstaff sediments were laid down on a relatively flat surface.

On most of the surrounding land surface, deposition of flood-plain sediments of the North Horn formation continued, as it had previously on the area now occupied by the lake. As was noted, North Horn sediments sometimes invaded the area of the lake and were later covered by lacustrine sediments.

An outstanding exception to this general statement is the area of Sixmile Canyon, where an island of considerable size was formed by the truncated edges of almost vertical Cretaceous rocks. The lower and middle Flagstaff beds (units

1 and 2) are absent, and the upper Flagstaff beds (unit 3) are deposited directly on the Cretaceous.

SOURCE OF SEDIMENTS: In early Flagstaff time a variety of previously deposited rocks was available to supply sediments to the Flagstaff lake. Spieker (1949, p. 78) has listed the crustal movements which preceded Flagstaff time in central Utah. They suggest a variety of outcropping rocks in early Flagstaff time within the drainage basin of the Flagstaff lake. The fact that the subunits of unit 1 are mainly limestone and fine clastic rocks indicates that they were derived mainly from the North Horn formation, which was the main outcropping formation in the immediate vicinity of the lake. If this is correct, a different source became available for the sediments of unit 2, which are markedly different in composition from those of unit 1.

NATURE OF SEDIMENTS: Unit 1 of the Flagstaff consists of irregularly bedded limestones and shales; individual beds range in thickness from less than 1 inch to more than 5 feet with some exceptionally thick shales 60–70 feet thick. These beds are highly calcareous, almost without exception; even the few sandstones in the section have a calcareous cement. In individual sections of limited lateral extent, the limestones and shales appear to alternate regularly from bottom to top. Where exposures are extensive enough, the individual beds thicken and thin laterally or merge. Such abrupt lateral variations indicate deposition in a shallow lake where wave action caused much shifting of the bottom muds. They would not have occurred in deep lakes, where deposition takes place far below wave base.

These conditions are characteristic of unit 1 in all parts of the Wasatch Plateau; the lateral and vertical variation is a prominent feature of this unit which is not displayed in the middle unit of the formation.

Such conditions indicate that the bottom of the lake was soft during early Flagstaff time, that it consisted of soft limy and clayey muds agitated by waves and currents, and that the waters of the lake had considerable turbidity because of a comparatively heavy load of fine clastic material.

WAVE ACTION: In a body of water the size of the Flagstaff lake the wind has a tremendous sweep, and waves form, whatever the direction or force of the wind. Since the lake was shallow, wave action affected the bottom over large portions of the lake area, possibly its entire extent. As a result, sediments were laid down unevenly over the bottom of the lake, as witness the lateral variation and the ripple marks preserved in many beds. This agitation resulted in turbidity, and we may picture the waters of the lake as muddy and sediment-laden, a condition which may have prevented some groups of the Mollusca from living in the lake. The preponderance of gill-breathing over lung-breathing forms may be explained by the good aeration of the lake water caused by wave action.

EVAPORATION: The consistently high calcium carbonate content of unit 1 beds requires explanation. Accounting for the source of the calcium carbonate presents no particular difficulty, for limy materials were available in quantity on the land surrounding the lake, and the calcium carbonate would naturally be brought into the lake by streams. The calcium carbonate precipitated as its concentration in the lake waters became high. The simplest and most natural cause to produce the required concentration seems to be evaporation of part of the water of the lake and the action of calcareous algae. If algae had been responsible for most of the precipitation of calcium carbonate in the lake, abundant traces of their existence should be found. This is the case for the Green River formation which contains large algal "reefs" at various zones. Since no such abundance of algae is found in unit 1 of the Flagstaff, the concentration of calcium carbonate in the lake must be attributed to evaporation. The only calcareous algae in the Flagstaff are the charophytes which are represented in the fossil assemblage but in altogether too small quantities to account exclusively for the precipitation of large quantities of calcium carbonate.

The concentrations of calcium carbonate would require a warm, semiarid climate. Some evidence on this point may be drawn from the land snails forming an incidental part of the unit 1 fauna. All of them are capable of living in a semiarid environment, and some, the bulimulids particularly, now live far south of Utah. If we grant the existence of a semiarid climate in central Utah in early Flagstaff time, high evaporation from the lake's extensive surface can be accepted, and the deposition of calcium carbonate in large quantities is easily understood.

VEGETATION: The only identifiable remains of plants in the Lower Flagstaff formation are oögonia of charophytes, described by Peck and Reker (1948). They are not common in the formation as a whole, and only a few beds contain concentrations of them. The carbon in the unit 1 beds may be due to washing into the lake of highly organic soil. Part of the carbon content of the formation is undoubtedly due to this source, but another part is certainly derived from water weeds that grew in the lake. Otherwise, it would be hard to imagine how some of the pulmonates could survive in this environment. Living species of *Gyraulus, Physa,* and lymnaeids abound on water weed which permits them to climb to the surface to breathe air occasionally and at least some areas of the lake may have had an abundance of such vegetation.

The microscopic flora of the lake must also have been abundant, for the majority of the Mollusca in the fauna feed on microscopic plants, especially algae. Since the concentration of mollusks is very high in places, probably their plant food was correspondingly abundant.

COMPOSITION OF THE MOLLUSCAN FAUNA: The main elements of the molluscan fauna of unit 1 are the fresh-water pelecypods and gastropods. Rare land snails, undoubtedly washed into the lake from the surrounding land or from islands in the lake, form only a very small percentage of the fauna. Detailed ecological summaries have been given for each molluscan genus in the section on systematic paleontology. They should be borne in mind for the discussion that follows.

The pelecypods belong in two groups, the Naiades and the Sphaeriidae. The Naiades are represented by a single species, *Elliptio mendax* (White), which may form as much as 16 per cent of the total individuals and 60 per cent of total volume in significant collections. The presence of only one species of naiad in present-day lakes is not unusual even if neighboring bodies of water contain species belonging to several genera. It is an interesting coincidence that in many northern lakes of the Canadian Shield area, the only genus represented in some lakes is also *Elliptio*. This scarcity may be explained by the peculiar environmental requirements of the Naiades. Not only is each species restricted somewhat in its habitat preferences, but it also requires the presence of a fish—in some cases a particular species of fish—to complete its life cycle. The larval naiades, called glochidia, are hatched within the gills of the parent clam and are ejected forcefully when a fish of the required species approaches the gravid female. The lucky glochidia attach themselves to the gills of the fish and live there for a considerable length of time, encysting completely into the tissues of the fish. After a period of time which varies from species to species, they work their way out, drop to the bottom, and begin their adult life, providing they emerged over a suitable environment. The unlucky glochidia which do not manage to attach themselves to the gills of a fish die in a very short time. Because of this curious feature of their life cycle, the naiad must inhabit an environment which is also attractive to its fish host. Shallow lakes have a limited fish fauna, and it is not surprising, therefore, to find a correspondingly small number of naiad species in them.

Two genera of sphaeriids, *Sphaerium* and *Pisidium,* are represented by at least one species each but not in large numbers. It is hard to explain their scarcity, for they are commonly abundant in present-day faunas, and their dispersal does not require the intervention of a temporary fish host. The only possible explanation that can be suggested is the strong wave action which has been assumed for the early Flagstaff lake. Most species of sphaeriids prefer a quieter environment which permits them to remain half buried in the mud, through which they plow slowly in their search for food. If the disturbance of the bottom by wave action is invoked to explain their scarcity, it may also apply, although in less degree, for the naiads. Wave action in the early Flagstaff lake may have been strong enough to discourage colonization by the sphaeriids but not quite enough to prevent the establishment of the naiad.

The gastropods of the unit 1 fauna may be divided into gill breathers and lung breathers. There are several genera of each. Gill breathers are more numerous and represent a larger percentage of the volume than the lungbreathers; in present-day lakes, in North America or elsewhere, the lung breathers predominate. No satisfactory ecological explanation can be advanced for this situation, and only two possibilities suggest themselves. First, the more vigorous and aggressive stocks of the lymnaeids and planorbids may not have appeared in Paleocene time. Second, the turbidity of the waters of the early Flagstaff lake may have made that environment unfavorable for lung breathers.

The gill breathers belong to the genera *Viviparus, Lioplacodes, Hydrobia, Micropyrgus,* and *Goniobasis.* These, judging by their living relatives, throve in turbid, wave-agitated waters on soft, muddy bottoms. Some show equal or greater partiality for other environments. For example, *Goniobasis* is equally at home in clear, well-aerated streams, and *Hydrobia* thrives on water weed from the surface to the bottom of a shallow lake. The most reliable ecological indicator in the group is *Viviparus,* which thrives best in shallow water, on a mud bottom, and is not commonly found elsewhere. It does not thrive in swiftly flowing waters nor on rocky, exposed shores. Its abundance in unit 1 supports the assumptions made on the basis of the lithology and the relative scarcity of sphaeriids.

Species of *Gyraulus, Carinulorbis, Ferrissia,* and *Physa* are certainly lung breathers. *Pleurolimnaea tenuicosta* (Meek and Hayden) is almost certainly a lung breather also, although its systematic position is uncertain. Judging by their living analogues, these mollusks should have been as much at home in the environment of the early Flagstaff lake as the more abundant gill breathers, but they were not. Possible explanations of this situation have been given at the beginning of this section.

Land snails form a small proportion of unit 1 assemblages. They indicate that a rich and varied molluscan population existed in early Flagstaff time with corresponding variety of environments. The early Flagstaff land snails belong to the species: *"Helix" riparia* White, *Carychium* cf. *C. exile* H. C. Lea, *Albertanella minuta* Russell, *Gastrocopta?* sp., and *Holospira* cf. *H. leidyi* (Meek).

VARIATION OF THE MOLLUSCAN FAUNA: The relative abundance of species varies vertically and horizontally in unit 1 of the Flagstaff. To ascertain the amount of variation, extensive collections were made in every fossiliferous unit of selected sections. The Ephraim section, collections 15 to 24, shows the amount of vertical variation in one place; comparison of several sections in the Wasatch Plateau shows the lateral variation. The most striking result of these analyses is the homogeneity of the fauna of unit 1 and its distinctness from that of unit 3. The break in faunas is somewhere between the top of unit 1 and the bottom of unit 3. The significance of this break for correlation and age will be discussed later.

Vertical variation within unit 1 is shown for the Ephraim section, which was most intensively collected. The samples were large enough (100 to more than 1700 specimens) to ensure that most of the species present should be represented in such numbers that their relative abundance could be plotted with a fair degree of certainty. In this section the most abundant species in all collections is *Hydrobia utahensis* White (32 to 91 per cent of individuals, 1.5 to 84 per cent of volume). All the others are represented in smaller proportions; some of them are particularly common in some units and rare in others. *Pleurolimnaea tenuicosta* (Meek and Hayden) is also represented in all units but in smaller numbers than *H. utahensis* White. *Micropyrgus minutulus* (Meek and Hayden), a species very similar to *Hydrobia utahensis* in shape and size, appears in seven units of the section and reaches its peak of abundance in unit 17. It may be significant that *Hydrobia utahensis* White is scarcer where *Micropyrgus minutulus* (Meek and Hayden) is more abundant. *Gyraulus militaris* (White) is represented in seven units but in small proportions and not localized in any particular part of the section. The sphaeriids are scarce, *Pisidium* sp. undet. is found in five units, and *Sphaerium* cf. *S. formosum* (Meek and Hayden) in two. This is rather surprising, considering the ease with which these genera are disseminated, but ecological factors, discussed under Composition of the Molluscan Fauna, may be responsible for the scarcity. *Lioplacodes mariana* Yen is found in four units, but the units are not grouped in a particular part of the section, and the species reaches its peak near the middle of the section, in unit 20.

There seems to be no significant variation from north to south or from east to west in our unit 1 collections. The Ephraim Canyon section yielded the greatest number of species, because it was the most thoroughly sampled section. The small number of species recorded for Fairview and Canal canyons to the north and for Musinia Peak to the south is due to the small number of samples obtained from these sections.

The species most widely distributed areally are *Hydrobia utahensis, Viviparus trochiformis,* and *Lioplacodes tenuicarinata,* but several others (Table 1) are only a little less widespread. It appears, therefore, that ecological conditions within the early Flagstaff lake had a narrow range of variation, and that this variation obtained throughout the area of the lake.

TABLE 1.—*Areal distribution of species in the lower part of the Flagstaff formation*

Species	1	2	3	4	5	6	7	8	9	10	11	Total
Elliptio mendax (White)	x		x	x	x		x					5
Sphaerium cf. *S. formosum* (Meek and Hayden)				x	x			x				3
Pisidium sp.				x	x							2
Viviparus trochiformis (Meek and Hayden)	x	x	x	x	x	x	x	x	x		x	10
Lioplacodes limnaeiformis (Meek and Hayden)						x			x			2
Lioplacodes mariana Yen			x	x	x	x	x			x		6
Lioplacodes tenuicarinata (Meek and Hayden)		x	x	x	x		x		x	x		7
Goniobasis tenera (Hall), form A			x		x	x	x					4
Goniobasis tenera (Hall), form D					x							1
Hydrobia utahensis White	x		x	x	x	x	x	x	x	x		9
Hydrobia cf. *H. recta* White			x			x	x					3
Micropyrgus minutulus (Meek and Hayden)				x	x		x	x		x		5
Pleurolimnaea tenuicosta (Meek and Hayden)			x	x	x		x	x		x		6
Gyraulus militaris White				x	x		x	x		x		5
Carinulorbis utahensis La Rocque						x			x	x		3
Physa bridgerensis Meek	x						x		x			3
Physa cf. *P. longiuscula* (Meek and Hayden)											x	1
Physa cf. *P. rhomboidea* (Meek and Hayden)			x									1
Physa sp. undet.			x	x		x					x	4
Ferrissia actinophora (White)						x						1
Ferrissia sp. A						x						1
Ferrissia sp. B						x						1
Carychium cf. *C. exile* H. C. Lea						x						1
"*Helix*" *riparia* White		x	x						x		x	4
Holospira cf. *H. leidyi* (Meek)								x				1
Discus cf. *D. ralstonensis* (Cockerell)						x					x	2
Gastrocopta sp.						x						1
Albertanella minuta Russell						x						1

1, Fairview Canyon, coll. 3
2. Canal Canyon, combined lists of species for colls. 4 and 5
3. The Horseshoe, combined lists of species for colls. 7–12
4. Pigeon Hollow, combined lists of species for colls. 13 and 14
5. Ephraim Canyon, combined lists of species for colls. 15–28
6. Willow Canyon, combined lists of species for colls. 30–32
7. Manti Canyon, combined lists of species for colls. 33–39
8. Wagon Road Ridge, coll. 41
9. Twelvemile Canyon, combined lists of species for colls. 42 and 43
10. Musinia Peak, combined lists of species for colls. 46 and 47
11. Pavant Range, coll. 53
Total. Number of localities in which the species is represented

MIDDLE FLAGSTAFF ENVIRONMENT

SIZE OF THE LAKE: In the second phase of its development the Flagstaff lake expanded far beyond its original area and covered what is now the Gunnison Plateau and the Long Ridge to the west and vast areas to the north and south and probably to the east also. The lower beds of the formation in the Gunnison Plateau are correlated with unit 2 of the Wasatch Plateau, and these beds in turn are believed to be coeval with the lower beds of the formation to the north, west, and south in the area indicated on Figure 2. Thus, the area of the lake more than doubled in Middle Flagstaff time.

DEPTH OF WATER: The rapid expansion of the lake was certainly accompanied by a deepening of the waters in its older portions. These deeper parts were gradually filled with sediments. The newer parts of the lake were shallow during at least part of Middle Flagstaff time, for ripple marks and even mud cracks formed then. There was also considerable variation in depth, for the North Horn surface newly covered by the lake had the characteristic unevenness of flood plains.

CHEMICAL COMPOSITION OF THE WATER: The chemical composition of the water changed radically when the lake expanded. The proportion of dissolved calcium carbonate may have been as high as it was previously, but a large proportion of gypsum in solution was added, as indicated by the abundance of that mineral in the rocks. The gypsum in the lake water undoubtedly contributed to the extinction of the molluscan population, during Middle Flagstaff time. Other forms of life probably suffered the same fate. Gypsum was present in the lake waters throughout Middle Flagstaff time, as it was deposited continuously, although in varying quantities. If the waters of the lake ever became suitable for Mollusca during this time, they remained so for too short a time to permit colonization of any extent; fresh-water forms are almost absent from the Middle Flagstaff.

FLUCTUATIONS OF THE SHORE LINE: No trace of red beds has been detected in the Middle Flagstaff of the Wasatch Plateau, although they are conspicuous in the Gunnison Plateau and the Long Ridge. The shore line apparently fluctuated during this time because of variation in the amount of water brought into the lake, the amount of evaporation from its surface, or because of a lowering of lake level caused by the cutting down of the outlet or outlets.

SURROUNDING LAND SURFACE: The exact nature of the land surface along the margins of the Flagstaff lake in its second phase is not known, but the sediments laid down during that time give some indication of its nature. The land surface had low relief, for the rocks consist of fine clastic materials and evaporites, with the exception of basal conglomerates in the western part of the Gunnison Plateau and in the Long Ridge. The island in the Sixmile Canyon area persisted throughout Middle Flagstaff time.

SOURCE OF SEDIMENTS: The newly expanded lake apparently covered most of the area of outcrop of the North Horn formation, for sediments conceivably derived from this source are present in the Middle Flagstaff only in patches around the margin of the lake. Since the Middle Flagstaff contains appreciable amounts of gypsum, the Jurassic Arapien formation was probably an important source of this mineral along with fine clastic materials and calcium carbonate. Certainly, the source of sediments during this time was very different from that supposed for early Flagstaff time, for the rocks are strikingly different.

NATURE OF SEDIMENTS: The lithology of the Middle Flagstaff contrasts strongly with that of the Lower Flagstaff. The dark-gray limestones and shales of the Lower Flagstaff are overlain by dazzling white clayey or marly massive limestones containing a large amount of gypsum. Probably they accumulated in deeper water, far from the margins of the lake, and were not affected by fluctuating lake level. These conditions indicate a quiet environment of deposition, below wave base, in which accumulation was steady and slow. The bottom of the lake in the region of the Wasatch Plateau was probably soft but less turbid than in early Flagstaff time.

WAVE ACTION: The size of the lake during Middle Flagstaff time had at least doubled, so that the sweep of the wind over its surface was probably greater than during its first phase. Wave action was still strong along the margins of the lake, but in the deeper central portion, over the present Wasatch Plateau, neither ripple marks nor mud cracks are found except near the top of this part of the Flagstaff.

EVAPORATION: Deposition of calcium carbonate continued, accompanied by the deposition of gypsum. Evaporation was probably greater than it had been previously. No evidence of calcareous algae has been found in the middle Flagstaff, but this is natural in view of the greater depth of the water.

VEGETATION: The Flagstaff lake in its middle phase must have been singularly barren of vegetation, possibly because of the chemical nature of the lake waters. If organic material in the form of soil was washed into the lake, there is no evidence of it in the carbon content of the rocks. Likewise, the bottom of the lake at this time was probably not covered with water weeds, for neither fragments of such weeds nor disseminated organic matter are present in the rocks. If a microscopic flora existed in the lake it has left no trace.

COMPOSITION OF THE MOLLUSCAN FAUNA: Only rare land snails are found in unit 2 of the Flagstaff. In the Wasatch Plateau area their scarcity implies rafting from the surrounding land or from small islands in the lake. Around the margins of the lake they are more abundant and occur in groups at the bottom of the formation as well as in the underlying North Horn formation. This suggests that they lived where they are preserved or not far away, and that they were either drowned as the lake rose or were dead when the lake waters reached them. No fresh-water mollusks have been found in this part of the formation in such assemblages as those of units 1 and 2 of the Flagstaff. A few rare and commonly fragmentary specimens were obviously carried in, probably from unit 1 of the Flagstaff which was eroded as the lake advanced over it.

LATE FLAGSTAFF ENVIRONMENT

SIZE OF THE LAKE: The second phase of the Flagstaff lake passed imperceptibly into the third with the gradual decrease of the gypsum content of its waters. This is reflected by a gradual passage from argillaceous limestones with a large amount of gypsum to argillaceous limestones with little, if any, gypsum. With the reduction of gypsum content the limestones also become noticeably thinner-bedded, indicating that the lake became shallower and possibly smaller. During the third phase the lake was probably as large as it had been in the second, but it probably included several islands and may have been divided into several small lakes intermittently connected with one another. Flood-plain sediments further restricted the size of the lake by invading its margins, as in the Gunnison Plateau, where the upper Flagstaff fauna is found in the Lower Colton formation, at several places above appreciable thicknesses of green, red, and variegated shales. The red color of the middle subunit of unit 3 south of Twelvemile Canyon may be due to the pouring in of red clastic sediments in relatively minor quantities. During late Flagstaff time, the lake varied in size, and before the close of late Flagstaff time it had vanished from much of its former area.

DEPTH OF WATER: The same factors which indicate that the early Flagstaff lake was shallow can be used to show that the late Flagstaff lake was also shallow. Common occurrence of mud cracks indicates intermittent drying of parts of the lake and ripple-marks are more common than in the lower part of the Flagstaff. The Mollusca are as abundant as in the lower part of the Flagstaff, in some beds more so, and accumulations of shell fragments, almost a coquina, are found in many places. The lateral and vertical variation of the beds is as great as in the lower part of the Flagstaff. Thick beds of limestone are few in the upper part of the Flagstaff; in the Wasatch Plateau, the thickest one observed was slightly less than 10 feet thick, and the thickness decreased to less than 5 feet in about 40 feet laterally. It seems safe to assume, therefore, that the Flagstaff lake was shallower at this time and that it was especially suited for hardy forms, such as *Physa,* which can survive for a long time out of water.

CHEMICAL COMPOSITION OF THE WATER: In the final phase, lake conditions were similar to those of the first phase. The streams flowing into the lake again brought in much dissolved calcium carbonate, and this was deposited on the bottom of the lake as concentrations became excessive. The proportion of dissolved gypsum remained low during late Flagstaff time, in strong contrast to the high proportion of middle Flagstaff time. Large amounts of dissolved silica were brought into the lake, as attested by numerous chert nodules.

FLUCTUATIONS OF THE SHORE LINE: In several places, major encroachments of red sediments, assigned to the Colton formation, invaded the Flagstaff lake in its last phase. All along the western margin of the Wasatch Plateau, south of Fairview Canyon, Colton sediments in varying thicknesses overlie the Flagstaff. North of Fairview Canyon, the Colton thins appreciably, and in the Soldier Summit area the Flagstaff grades without interruption into the Green River formation. These relationships indicate a constantly fluctuating shore line and a constantly shrinking area for the Flagstaff lake in its final phase.

SURROUNDING LAND SURFACE: The fine grain of the sediments from the upper part of the Flagstaff indicates that the surrounding land had low relief and streams carried only small quantities of the finest clastic materials into the lake. The island in the Sixmile Canyon area was covered by the lake in late Flagstaff time.

SOURCE OF SEDIMENTS: Only minor amounts of fine clastic materials, possibly derived from reworked flood-plain sediments, were laid down in the lake during its last phase. However, streams brought much dissolved calcium carbonate to the lake. The exact source of these materials is indeterminable, but they were derived from some of the older formations of the region, many of which are rich in calcium carbonate.

NATURE OF SEDIMENTS: The upper part of the Flagstaff consists of thin-bedded white to gray limestones with minor amounts of shale; there are chert nodules at several levels, and some of the beds are highly silicified. The unit as a whole is constant laterally but extremely variable in detail, both vertically and laterally. These lithologic characteristics indicate a return to the conditions of early Flagstaff time, namely soft limy muds, but with less clay and more silica.

WAVE ACTION: The lake was larger in late Flagstaff time than in early Flagstaff time, but its shallower depth reduced the power of wave action. Sediments were still laid down unevenly, as indicated by the lateral variation of the beds and their thinness, but gentler wave action probably resulted in less turbidity and less effective aeration of the water. This may be the reason that some of the gill breathers, particularly *Lioplacodes* and *Hydrobia*, are not represented in the upper part of the Flagstaff. An alternative explanation is suggested under the section on Vegetation.

EVAPORATION: Indications are that evaporation took place at a high rate in the last phase of the lake. Land snails are few in the upper part of the Flagstaff of the Wasatch Plateau, but the same conclusions may be drawn from them as for the early Flagstaff lake.

VEGETATION: One of the few constant characteristics which distinguish the upper from the lower part of the Flagstaff is the absence of dark beds in the former and their ubiquitous presence in the latter. The dark coloring of the lower part of the Flagstaff is probably due to carbon derived from vegetation, either in the lake itself or brought in with sediments. If so, entirely different conditions must be assumed for the late Flagstaff. The supposition would fit well with the situation in some extant shallow lakes which are almost free of water weeds. Absence of water weed would make the environment less suitable for the amnicoloid snails (for example, *Hydrobia*); this may have a direct bearing on the scarcity of members of that genus in the upper part of the Flagstaff as compared with their abundance in the lower part of the Flagstaff. The same factor may also be responsible for the absence of *Lioplacodes,* but in this case the lack of complete aeration in the shallow waters of the lake appears to be the more probable explanation. Lack of abundant vegetation may also be responsible for the absence in the upper part of the Flagstaff of other species present in the lower part of the formation, but speculation on this point is hazardous.

COMPOSITION OF THE MOLLUSCAN FAUNA: The molluscan fauna of the upper part of the Flagstaff, as that of the lower part of the Flagstaff, comprises freshwater pelecypods and gastropods and rare land snails.

The Naiades are represented by two genera, *Elliptio* and *Lampsilis,* but the species are different from those of the lower part of the Flagstaff. The Naiades form as much as 11 per cent of the total individuals and 28 per cent of total volume in representative collections.

The Sphaeriidae are represented by a single genus and species, *Sphaerium* cf. *S. formosum* (Meek and Hayden), which is also found in the lower part of the Flagstaff, where it is accompanied by a species of *Pisidium*. No special paleoecological significance is attached to this variation.

The aquatic gill-breathing gastropods are represented in the upper part of the Flagstaff by *Viviparus paludinaeformis* (Hall), *Goniobasis tenera* (Hall), form B, and *Hydrobia ephraimensis* La Rocque. Together, they may form as much as 52 per cent of the total individuals and 40 per cent of the total volume in representative collections. *Lioplacodes* and *Micropyrgus* are absent from the upper part of the Flagstaff, but the other gill breathers belong to the same genera as those of the lower part of the Flagstaff. Their relative abundance and inferred ecological preferences indicate that the conditions of the early Flagstaff lake were now renewed, and that the lake was colonized by forms most at home in shallow water with a muddy bottom. No ecological significance is attached to the absence of *Lioplacodes* and *Micropyrgus* from these assemblages.

The aquatic lung-breathing gastropods belong to the species *Gyraulus militaris* (White), *G. aequalis* (White), *Physa pleromatis* White, *Physa* sp. undet., and *Ferrissia actinophora* (White). These genera are also present in the lower Flagstaff assemblages. They may form up to 45 per cent of total individuals and 56 per cent of total volume in upper Flagstaff collections. The absence of *Carinulorbis* and *Pleurolimnaea* from the upper part of the Flagstaff seems to have no paleoecological implications.

Land snails are about as scarce in the upper as in the lower part of the Flagstaff and are too scarce for paleoecological conclusions. They belong to the species *Discus* cf. *D. ralstonensis* (Cockerell), *"Helix" riparia* White, *Bulimulus?* sp., and *Holospira* cf. *H. leidyi* (Meek).

VARIATION OF THE MOLLUSCAN FAUNA: Stratigraphically superposed assemblages were available for only one section (Fairview Canyon, collections 1 and 2). In this locality vertical variation in the fauna is considerable, changing from 3 to 10 species in 10 feet. In the other sections the upper part of the Flagstaff contains a molluscan assemblage in only one unit, and the remainder of the section yielded only rare fragments of Mollusca.

The most extensive representation of the upper Flagstaff fauna is in the northern part of the area, in Fairview Canyon (collection 1) and Ephraim Canyon (collection 29). This pattern strongly suggests a migration into the lake from the north, especially as the fossiliferous units in each section are lithologically the same. This conclusion must be accepted with reservations, since the stratigraphic equivalence of the units in question cannot be established with certainty.

The species most widely distributed areally are *Viviparus paludinaeformis* (Hall) and *Goniobasis tenera* (Hall), form B, represented in six and five collections respectively. *Physa pleromatis* White is represented in four collections, and the other species in three or less (Table 2). This distribution points to a wide range of variation in ecological conditions in the late Flagstaff lake; this variation is not reflected in the lithology.

TABLE 2.—*Areal distribution of species in the upper part of the Flagstaff formation*

Species	1	2	29	38	40	45	Total
Elliptio mormonum La Rocque....................	x	..	x	..	..	..	2
Lampsilis spiekeri La Rocque......................	x	..	..	..	..	..	1
Sphaerium cf. *S. formosum* (Meek and Hayden)....	x	..	x	..	..	..	2
Viviparus paludinaeformis (Hall).................	x	x	x	x	x	x	6
Goniobasis tenera (Hall), form B..................	x	..	x	x	x	x	5
Hydrobia ephraimensis La Rocque.................	..	..	x	..	..	..	1
Gyraulus militaris (White)........................	x	..	x	x	..	..	3
Gyraulus aequalis (White).........................	..	..	x	x	..	..	2
Physa pleromatis White...........................	x	x	x	x	..	..	4
Physa, sp. undet...................................	x	..	x	..	..	..	2
Ferrissia actinophora (White).....................	x	..	x	..	..	..	2
"*Helix*" *riparia* White.............................	..	x	..	x	x	..	3
Discus cf. *D. ralstonensis* (Cockerell)..............	x	..	..	..	..	..	1

1. Fairview Canyon, coll. 1
2. Fairview Canyon, coll. 2
29. Ephraim Canyon, coll. 29
38. Manti Canyon, coll. 38
40. Sixmile Canyon, coll. 40
45. Twelvemile Canyon, coll. 45
Total. Number of localities in which the species is represented

CORRELATION AND AGE

Table 3 shows the species found in the Flagstaff formation. The list contains Paleocene and Eocene elements; the known Paleocene species occur in unit 1, the known Eocene species in unit 3. This suggests a Paleocene age for unit 1 and an Eocene age for unit 3. No definite age determination for unit 2 is possible at present, because diagnostic fossils are absent.

The list consists of 37 recognizable forms, of which 27 are identifiable as to species, 7 of them doubtfully. There are 4 new species. Only 4 species are found in two or more units of the formation: *Gyraulus militaris* (White) in units 1 and 3, *"Helix" riparia* White in all three units, *Holospira* cf. *H. leidyi* (Meek) in units 2 and 3, *Discus* cf. *D. ralstonensis* (Cockerell) in units 1 and 3. The first of these is a fresh-water snail, much more abundant in unit 3 than in unit 1, and it is considered as an early invader in the Wasatch Plateau region which later became much more abundant. Its presence in unit 1 is not considered sufficient grounds for assigning that unit to the Eocene. The same may be said for the other three species in this group, all land snails and inconspicuous elements of the fauna, of sporadic occurrence.

The faunas of units 1 and 3 are distinct and recognizable, even in the field or with an incomplete representation of the fauna. Twenty-one species, of which seven are relatively common, are present in unit 1 and absent from the other two units. Ten species, of which five are relatively common, are present in unit 3 and absent from the other two units.

Assignment of unit 1 to the Paleocene is based on: (1) the occurrence of *Pleurolimnaea tenuicosta* (Meek and Hayden) and *Albertanella minuta* Russell, both recorded so far only for the Paleocene; (2) affinities of the fauna with that of the North Horn formation—they both contain *Viviparus trochiformis* (Meek and Hayden), *Hydrobia* cf. *H. recta* White, and perhaps other species as well, although the North Horn material on which this statement is based is poorly preserved; (3) the presence in unit 1 and absence in unit 3 of the following species, recorded for Paleocene and Eocene beds elsewhere: *Viviparus trochiformis* (Meek and Hayden), *Lioplacodes limnaeiformis* (Meek and Hayden), *L. mariana* Yen, and *L. tenuicarinata* (Meek and Hayden); (4) the occurrence in unit 1 and not in unit 3 of additional species of Paleocene aspect: *Elliptio mendax* (White), *Hydrobia utahensis* White, *Micropyrgus minutulus* (Meek and Hayden), and *Carinulorbis utahensis* La Rocque. This assignment is in harmony with the geologic relationships of unit 1 which intertongues with the Paleocene part of the North Horn formation.

Assignment of unit 3 to the Eocene is based on the following considerations: (1) occurrence in it and not in unit 1 of the Eocene species *Gyraulus aequalis* (White) and *Physa pleromatis* White; (2) absence in unit 3 of undoubted Paleocene elements. This assignment is also in harmony with the geologic rela-

73

tionships of unit 3, which intertongues with the Colton formation. The fauna of the Colton formation is decidedly Eocene in character. The lacustrine beds of the Colton contain species identical with those of unit 3 and, as might be expected, none of the Paleocene elements of unit 1.

The fauna of unit 1 is very similar in composition to several others of Paleocene age, of which a few examples may be cited. In the Tongue River member of the Fort Union formation, Yen (1948b, p. 36) found *Viviparus trochiformis* (Meek and Hayden), *Lioplacodes mariana* Yen, *L. limnaeiformis* (Meek and Hayden), *L. tenuicarinata* (Meek and Hayden), *Pleurolimnaea tenuicosta* (Meek and Hayden), *Gyraulus militaris* (White), and *Sphaerium* cf. *S. formosum* (Meek and Hayden), all represented in unit 1 of the Flagstaff. In addition, the fauna also contains species of *Goniobasis, Ferrissia, Carinulorbis,* and *Elliptio* related to species of unit 1. In these beds, as in unit 1, *Pleurolimnaea tenuicosta* (Meek and Hayden) is confined to the Paleocene part of the formation, whereas *Viviparus trochiformis* (Meek and Hayden), the three species of *Lioplacodes,* and others persist into the overlying Wasatch formation.

TABLE 3.—*Occurrence of species in the Flagstaff formation*

Species	Unit 1	Unit 2	Unit 3
Elliptio mormonum La Rocque	0	0	x
Elliptio mendax (White)	x	0	0
Lampsilis spiekeri La Rocque	0	0	x
Sphaerium cf. *S. formosum* (Meek and Hayden)	x	0	x
Pisidium sp. undet.	x	0	0
Viviparus trochiformis (Meek and Hayden)	x	0	0
V. paludinaeformis (Hall)	0	0	x
Lioplacodes limnaeiformis (Meek and Hayden)	x	0	0
Lioplacodes mariana Yen	x	0	0
Lioplacodes tenuicarinata (Meek and Hayden)	x	0	0
Goniobasis tenera (Hall), form A	x	0	0
Goniobasis tenera (Hall), form B	0	0	x
Goniobasis tenera (Hall), form D	x	0	0
Hydrobia utahensis White	x	0	0
Hydrobia cf. *H. recta* White	x	0	0
Hydrobia ephraimensis La Rocque	0	0	x
Micropyrgus minutulus (Meek and Hayden)	x	0	0
Pleurolimnaea tenuicosta (Meek and Hayden)	x	0	0
Gyraulus militaris (White)	x	0	x
Gyraulus aequalis (White)	0	0	x
Carinulorbis utahensis La Rocque	x	0	0
Physa bridgerensis Meek	x	0	0
Physa pleromatis White	0	0	x
Physa cf. *P. longiuscula* Meek and Hayden	x	0	0
Physa cf. *P. rhomboidea* Meek and Hayden	x	0	0
Physa sp. undet.	x	0	x
Ferrissia actinophora (White)	0	0	x
Ferrissia? sp. A	x	0	0
Ferrissia? sp. B	x	0	0
Carychium cf. *C. exile* H. C. Lea	x	0	0
"*Helix*" *riparia* White	x	x	x
Oreohelix sp.	0	0	x
Bulimulus? sp.	0	0	x
Holospira cf. *H. leidyi* (Meek)	0	x	x
Discus cf. *D. ralstonensis* (Cockerell)	x	0	x
Gastrocopta? sp.	x	0	0
Albertanella minuta	x	0	0

Another fauna described by Yen (1946, p. 41–48) contains the same genera and some of the same species as those commonest in unit 1: *Viviparus, Lioplacodes, Hydrobia, Gyraulus, Carinulorbis,* and *Elliptio.* Several assemblages described by Russell (1926, p. 207–213) are of similar nature.

Early Eocene assemblages from Wyoming described by Yen (1948a, p. 636, collections W–1 and W–2) contain *Viviparus paludinaeformis* (Hall) and *Goniobasis tenera* (Hall), also present in Unit 3; collection W–1 also contains a *Ferrissia* similar to *F. actinophora* (White) of unit 3.

HISTORY OF THE FLAGSTAFF LAKE

GENERAL CONSIDERATIONS

REGIMEN OF LAKES: Lakes are impermanent features of the earth's surface. If they have no outlet, their extinction will come about by silting or evaporation. Lakes with an outlet are on their way to certain extinction in a period of time measurable by the rate at which the outlet deepens its bed. Other causes may also contribute to the extinction of a lake. Vegetation gradually fills its bed, restricts its extent by building shallows, permitting first marsh vegetation and then meadow plants to grow. Rarely, as in the shallow lakes of the Great Basin area, extinction comes about through evaporation because of an insufficient increment of water from the lake's drainage basin. In most lakes, two or more factors contribute to the lake's extinction. A lake may be rejuvenated and expand if its outlet is blocked or its basin deepened by tectonic movements. Ultimately, however, all lakes are doomed to extinction.

A lake constitutes an enclave of peculiar nature in the general environment of a given region. Its shores are a haven for wading birds attracted by the fishes or amphibians living in the lake. It supports a population of reptiles, especially turtles, and serves as breeding ground for frogs, toads, and salamanders. Its shallows, once they have been prepared by the development of vegetation, support a teeming population of arthropods and mollusks, of annelids and wormlike animals, who feed on each other and on protozoans and minute plants. The hard parts of some of these animals are preserved in the sediments of the lake, and even after the lake has become extinct they provide a fascinating record of changing environment and the succession of life in the lacustrine environment.

The Flagstaff lake provides such a record for the late Paleocene and early Eocene. Study of its faunas and of the sediments in which they are preserved discloses three major periods in the development of the lake distinguished from each other by the materials deposited, mode of deposition, and composition of the molluscan fauna. These phases in the history of the lake will be described separately, but they grade imperceptibly into each other, and conditions which may long since have disappeared in one part of the lake remained in existence in another.

INTERPRETATION OF SEDIMENTS: Sedimentary sections of lacustrine origin and of considerable magnitude are rare in the accessible record of the earth's history. One point, among others, which attracts interest to the Flagstaff section is its great thickness. Here is the record of a lake of great extent and impressive longevity, displaying all the richness of detail which may be expected of it. Discussion of the stratigraphy has shown that the formation may be divided into three gross units, each lithologically recognizable. Each unit in turn presents variations worthy of attempted interpretation. It seems best, therefore, to attack each

77

problem separately and to see what information each lithologic sequence may yield concerning the life history of the lake.

The lowermost unit is composed of carbonaceous, alternating limy shales and silty limestones in thin beds, ranging from a few inches to several feet in thickness. This characteristic alternation is especially developed in the sections exposed in the many canyons of the central Wasatch Plateau but is absent in the surrounding areas, the Gunnison Plateau, the Valley and Pavant mountains, and even in the northern and southern thirds of the Wasatch Plateau itself. Stratigraphic evidence indicates that these are the oldest rocks of the Flagstaff formation and that they were also the first to form in the Flagstaff lake itself. The entire sequence is highly calcareous, has a high carbon content, and was produced by a single depositional episode, during which the deposition of silt and calcium carbonate varied abruptly in intensity. The sediments were deposited in shallow water. An obvious hypothesis for the alternation of limestone and shale in this section is that calcium carbonate deposition was continuous, since it is present in all units, and that the intensity of silt deposition varied. When little silt was being brought into the lake, predominantly limy beds were deposited; the reverse occurred to form the shaly beds. This hypothesis would account for the alternation of limestones and limy shales, but it presents grave difficulties when one seeks to reconstruct the source for the calcium carbonate and silt involved. What mechanism can regulate the alternate influx of silt and calcium carbonate into a lake basin? Both the precipitate and the fine silt are brought in by streams. How can the streams alternately furnish a great deal of calcium carbonate and little silt and then a great deal of silt and little calcium carbonate?

The behavior of present-day lakes (Kindle, 1927), with special consideration of the formation of marl, may be instructive. Kindle has shown that in present-day lakes, where marl is forming, it does not accumulate uniformly on the entire bed of the lake. It does so in shallow lakes, where thermal stratification is not possible, but in deep lakes marl accumulates only in the epilimnion, in shallow parts of the lake, especially in shallow bays. Moreover, the cross section of such a lake presents some curious features. Mollusca live in the shallower parts of the lake, and it is here that true shell marls are formed. In a zone beyond this depth marl still forms but shells are scarce. Beyond this, below the thermocline, is the bottom zone where only muds, not marls, accumulate. Let us imagine a shallow lake, too shallow for thermal stratification to establish itself. When the water of the lake is uniformly shallow, silt and marl, the first in larger quantities, are deposited and Mollusca thrive all over the lake bottom. If the water level of the lake is raised, silty muds are deposited only along the margins of the lake, and Mollusca thrive only there. In the central portions of the lake, more marl than silt is deposited, and Mollusca will not thrive; hence, their remains will be found only as rare fragments in the limy sediments. Let the level of the lake fluctuate from time to time, and alternating deposits of limy muds, abundantly fossiliferous, and silty limestones, with fewer fossils, will be formed.

This hypothesis requires a mechanism which will alternately raise and lower the level of the lake within narrow limits and over lengthy periods of time and which will be capable of repeating the effect hundreds of times. Stratigraphic evidence indicates that the Flagstaff lake had considerable extent and gradually extended its boundaries, especially after deposition of the lowermost unit. Spieker (1946, p. 160) has mentioned two possibilities in explanation, geosynclinal warping and movement of fault blocks. Geosynclinal movement would, in time, deepen the central portion in the Flagstaff lake. Such a deep part of the lake, perhaps correlated with the hypolimnion of a modern lake, would be indicated by thick, continuous shales, unbroken by limestone beds, and barren or nearly so of fossils. The thick shales at the top of the lower unit of the Flagstaff formation may be amenable to such interpretation, but there is nothing of this nature in the lower part of the unit, composed entirely of thin, alternating limestones and shales. On the other hand, movement of fault blocks during early Flagstaff time presents a more acceptable alternative.

Let us suppose that the original cause of the depression in which the waters of the initial Flagstaff lake collected was movement of fault blocks. This would not create a bowl-shaped depression such as would be expected of geosynclinal areas, but a great depressed area of uniform depth. From what we know of movement along fault blocks, whether from the evidence of faults active in historic times or from the sedimentary evidence of movement along ancient faults, such movement would not take place in one great displacement but in small pulses, a few feet at a time. This, together with the natural tendency of outlet streams to erode each time there is a rise in lake level or increased slope, would provide the mechanism to explain the alternating limestones and shales of the lower part of the Flagstaff.

For example, a small initial movement over a geographically extensive fault would give the initial shallow depression in which Flagstaff waters could first accumulate. Slow drainage by relatively sluggish streams would bring to this depression, from the North Horn flood plain around it, fine silt with only small amounts of sand and coarse clastic sediments around the margins of the lake. As the shallow lake would spread out in the depression thus created, mollusks would gradually colonize it. Before this could happen, however, a suitable period of time would have to elapse during which the substratum would be prepared by influx of water plants and minute invertebrates. Further movement of the fault block might cause the water to deepen to such an extent that molluscan life could no longer exist except along the shallow margins of the lake; only silty limestones could accumulate over most of the lake. Following uplift, the outlet streams would resume downcutting with renewed vigor and gradually lower the level of the outlet. Continued lowering of the level of the outlet would result in lowering of lake level, and silt could be carried to the central portions of the lake. Simultaneously, Mollusca could re-invade the shallower central portions of the lake until further movement along the fault again prevented it.

This explanation is intentionally oversimplified; it takes no account of fault movement other than that which would control the level of the Flagstaff lake, and it disregards those movements which permitted North Horn sediments to encroach on the Flagstaff lake from time to time. Yet it seems to explain satisfactorily the alternation of limestones and shales characteristic of the basal unit of the Flagstaff.

If this hypothesis is accepted, a number of corollaries may be derived. First, the entire sequence of the lower part of the Flagstaff would provide indirect evidence of early Flagstaff orogeny. Orogenic forces were active in the central Utah region long before Flagstaff time (Spieker, 1946; 1949). Spieker has shown evidence for pre-Flagstaff orogeny in the Sixmile Canyon area, but no evidence so far has been adduced for orogenic movement during Flagstaff time. Attribution of the unit 1 alternation of sediments to orogeny would require relatively small pulses. This would contrast sharply with the relatively stable conditions of middle Flagstaff time, and there is no particular similarity with those of late Flagstaff time.

Second, the peculiar vertical changes in molluscan assemblages would be explainable. Relatively rapid variation of lake level is bound to have its effect on molluscan population. Sudden raising of lake level establishes connections with near-by drainages which allow new forms of mollusks to invade the lake. Gradual lowering during the cutting down of the lake's outlet permits the spread of these species to almost all parts of the lake. But sudden raising of the level again causes the extinction of the greater part of the molluscan population, for the shallow margins of the lake, newly covered, are not immediately fit for molluscan habitation. The lake must be repopulated by new arrivals. Repopulation of the lake did take place several times, but each time the assemblage was somewhat different from its predecessors. There were times when no repopulation occurred, as witness several barren shales in the sequence which seem to be lithologically like those which bear such a heavy molluscan assemblage in the lower part of unit 1.

Another explanation has been suggested by F. H. McLearn (Personal communication). Large amounts of clastic materials would be deposited in the lake basin during prolonged rains, and small amounts would be deposited during dry periods. Calcium carbonate would be carried in by streams at all times, but the amount of clastic sediment would vary. This hypothesis is particularly attractive if it is assumed that the level of the lake at low water was below the level of the outlet. This would mean that evaporation would operate with much greater effect during periods of low water, and almost pure calcareous muds would be deposited. Greater rainfall would raise the level of the lake and increase the carrying power of its tributary streams, causing deposition of clastic sediments over the limy muds. These alternations are not considered seasonal—the thickness of the alternating beds seems too great for that—but as extending over a number of years, in fluctuations similar to those now observable in central Utah.

The deleterious effect on Mollusca of raising the level of a lake is not mere supposition. Numerous instances are cited in the literature of living Mollusca, and I have pointed out its effect on the molluscan fauna of one lake which I have studied in detail (La Rocque, 1935, p. 50). In this instance, Meach Lake, Quebec, only a few species of the molluscan fauna were affected. These species were eliminated from the assemblage by fluctuation of lake level. The others were able to survive thanks to their ability to adapt themselves to a wide range of depths or, perhaps, more simply, to high reproductive rate and a well-developed tendency to migrate. There are, therefore, modern instances of marked changes in lake populations due to changes in lake level.

ORIGIN OF THE FLAGSTAFF LAKE

The Flagstaff lake began by the formation of a depression in the area where its lowest beds are found—that is, in the southern Wasatch Plateau (Fig. 2)—and the accumulation in that depression of the water draining from the surrounding regions. The depression is not hard to account for; the entire region covered by the Flagstaff lake was one of crustal instability. Spieker (1949, p. 78-79) recognized six distinct crustal movements before the inception of the Flagstaff lake, and it may reasonably be assumed that they produced an extremely uneven surface in which one or more lake basins could have formed.

The Flagstaff lake was not the first to exist in the region; many lacustrine beds exist in the North Horn formation, both in its type locality, North Horn Mountain, and in the east flank of the Gunnison Plateau. Most of these earlier lakes had become extinct long before the beginning of the Flagstaff lake, for the lacustrine beds of the North Horn formation are almost everywhere separated from the lowest beds of the Flagstaff by thick flood-plain deposits. Some areas of lacustrine environment probably persisted from North Horn to Flagstaff time. The intimate relationship of the two faunas makes the assumption probable, but so far no exposed section has yielded an example of lacustrine North Horn beds grading into lacustrine Flagstaff beds.

In most exposures where the transition between the North Horn and the Flagstaff is visible, there is a thick sequence of lithologically constant blue-gray beds. Only the upper beds are fossiliferous. This sequence appears to represent the interval of time during which the lake bottom was being prepared, by vegetation and microfauna not preserved as fossils, for the invasion of abundant molluscan faunas which throve for a time in the lake and were then exterminated.

The Flagstaff lake originated during Paleocene time, not at the very end of that epoch, for the lower part of the Flagstaff represents a considerable portion of Paleocene time. In the Wasatch Plateau area at least, the Flagstaff lake precedes the Green River lake by many thousands of years, and much of its history antedates that of the Green River lake to the north.

VARIATIONS IN EXTENT

Figure 2 shows the character of the Flagstaff lake during most of its existence. It was a huge lake, much larger than most of those now in existence, and it compares in size with the Pleistocene Great Lakes which originated many millions of years later. Its western and northern boundaries can be traced with some accuracy, but the southern and eastern shore lines remain conjectural.

The southern boundary cannot be traced, partly because of the extensive volcanic beds under which the Flagstaff is concealed in the Salina region and southward, and partly because of the uncertainty of correlation between the Bryce Canyon beds and the Flagstaff. Even if a part of the Bryce Canyon beds could be correlated with the Flagstaff, some doubt would still exist regarding their continuity with the Flagstaff lake to the north. The Bryce Canyon beds are fluviatile, not lacustrine, so that their identity with the Flagstaff formation would not materially increase the size of the Flagstaff lake.

The eastern boundary has been destroyed by erosion, and only conjectures can be made about it. Spieker (1949, p. 31–32) notes he has "traced it to a vague remnant in the Sunnyside district; it may continue, invading en echelon the upper part of the North Horn formation, as far as Green River." In the area south of the West Tavaputs Plateau it is reasonable to suppose that the Flagstaff once extended at least half way between the east front of the Wasatch Plateau and the Green River.

The northern and western boundaries are more exactly known. They have been traced (Spieker, 1949, p. 31) by S. J. Muessig and A. A. Baker.

Known outcrops indicate that the Flagstaff lake had a minimum area of about 2800 square miles. If the area eroded away along its eastern margin is added, the probable maximum area was about 4000 square miles.

Whether or not the Flagstaff lake extended as one continuous body over this large area remains doubtful. Stratigraphic evidence shows that it began as a much smaller lake in the eastern part of the Wasatch Plateau and slowly spread in all directions until its maximum size was reached. The great continuity of the upper beds of the formation over wide areas indicates that, in the latter part of its existence at least, the Flagstaff lake formed an inland sea of imposing size which has no counterpart in North America at present. Its closest analogue is the Green River lake which followed it closely in time.

FIRST PHASE

The Flagstaff lake began, in late Paleocene time, as a body of water of modest size (Fig. 2) bounded either by fault scarps or the margins of a geosynclinal fold, more probably the former. The bottom of the lake was mainly the uneven surface of North Horn sediments which continued to accumulate along its margins and occasionally encroached upon the lake, notably in the Twelvemile and Pigeon Hollow areas.

There was at least one island in the lake at this stage, in the Sixmile Canyon area, where Cretaceous sedimentary rocks, folded in a previous orogeny, stood almost vertically, forming a rugged island in the lake. This island persisted throughout early Flagstaff time and was not submerged until late medial or early late Flagstaff time.

The sediments accumulated during this phase have already been described in this paper. Lake level fluctuated frequently and irregularly during this phase, as attested by the alternating limestones and limy shales characteristic of the lower part of the Flagstaff. The fluctuations had a marked influence on the molluscan fauna. During this phase, the lake was shallow enough to support abundant aquatic vegetation which has given its sediments a distinctive carbonaceous content.

The first phase of the lake ended rather abruptly with a raising of lake level and a great expansion of its area which brought into it sediments of a different nature from a new source.

SECOND PHASE

The Flagstaff lake expanded greatly at the beginning of this phase. The expansion was comparatively swift, so that the middle unit of the Flagstaff rests on North Horn and other sedimentary rocks in a very large area along the margins of the first-phase lake. The expansion covered the former sediment sources of the lake and brought new ones, of a different nature, into play. The fine dark clays, probably derived from North Horn sediments, were no longer brought into the lake. Instead, tan and light-gray sediments, probably derived from earlier Jurassic and Cretaceous rocks, gave the middle unit of the Flagstaff a distinctive light color.

The new sediment source included gypsum and salt which made the waters of the lake toxic to vegetation and animal life. The shallow margins of the expanded lake apparently were never suitable for the development of aquatic vegetation, and therefore the sediments accumulated in the lake at this time lack the higher carbon content of the lower unit.

The same toxicity was probably responsible for the extinction of the original molluscan fauna in the lake itself; some species may have survived in tributary streams, for they appear again, with some evolutionary modifications, in the upper unit.

The land-snail fauna continued to exist in the surrounding land area and probably also on islands in the lake. Land snails are found sparingly in the middle unit at several places (Ephraim, Wales, and Twelvemile canyons) which were far from the shores.

The second phase ended with a further and final expansion of the lake and the exhaustion or burial under lake sediments of the source of salt and gypsum.

THIRD PHASE

The sediments accumulated during the second phase had almost filled the deeper, original part of the lake. As a result, the Flagstaff lake, in spite of further expansion in the final phase of its development, was shallow.

The island in the Sixmile Canyon area was covered by sediments either late in the second phase or early in the third. At any rate, it is overlain by third-phase sediments.

The lake was populated early in this stage by a varied fresh-water fauna. The Mollusca throve in the area of the Wasatch and Gunnison plateaus, the Valley Mountains, and Cedar Hills, but did not reach the outer margins of the lake, probably because these had not yet been sufficiently prepared for them. In the marginal areas, land snails are common, possibly because their habitat was drowned out by the advancing lake and the shells were preserved in place.

The new molluscan fauna was generically similar to the old, although with some important exceptions which have been pointed out. It was a fauna of decidedly Eocene aspect, related more closely to that of the lacustrine Colton and Green River formations than to that of the lower part of the Flagstaff.

The existence of the lake at this time was precarious. It was repeatedly invaded by continental sediments of the Colton formation which encroached upon it extensively and finally obliterated most of it toward the end of the third phase.

EXTINCTION

The history of the Flagstaff lake ends not in total extinction but in partial obliteration by the invasion of Colton sediments and merging of the northern part of its basin with that of the Green River lake. The latter eventually occupied an area greater than that of the Flagstaff lake.

Lacustrine conditions were not entirely wiped out during Colton time; the Colton formation contains lacustrine beds of small extent but appreciable thickness which carry an abundant molluscan fauna. These beds cannot properly be called extensions of the Flagstaff, but the molluscan fauna which they carry was probably derived indirectly from the late Flagstaff fauna.

The northern remnant of the Flagstaff lake merged with the Green River lake advancing southward so that it did not, strictly speaking, end in extinction. Still, from the time of its junction with the Green River lake, it lost its identity, and its history may fittingly be closed at this point.

REFERENCES CITED

BAILEY, JOSHUA L., JR., (1929) *Fresh Water Mollusca in Brackish Water,* Nautilus, vol. 43, p. 34.

BAKER, FRANK C. (1911) *The Lymnaeidae of North and Middle America,* Chicago Acad. Sci., Spec. Publ. No. 3, 539 p., 58 Pls., 51 Figs.

—— (1928) *The Fresh Water Mollusca of Wisconsin,* Wis. Geol. and Nat. Hist. Surv., Bull. 70, Part I, Gastropoda, 507 p., 28 Pls.; Part II, Pelecypoda, 495 p., Pls. 29–105

CLENCH, WILLIAM J. (1926) *Three New Species of Physa,* Univ. Mich., Mus. Zool., Occas. Papers, No. 168, 8 p., 1 Pl.

COCKERELL, THEODORE D. A. (1906) *The Fossil Mollusca of Florissant, Colorado,* Am. Mus. Nat. Hist., Bull., vol. 22, p. 459–462

—— (1914) *Tertiary Mollusca from New Mexico and Wyoming,* Am. Mus. Nat. Hist., Bull., vol. 33, p. 101–107

DAWSON, JEAN (1911) *The Biology of* Physa, Behavior Monogr., vol. 1, No. 4, 120 p., 10 Figs.

GILLILAND, WILLIAM N. (1951) *Geology of the Gunnison Quadrangle, Utah,* Univ. Nebraska Studies, new series, no. 8, 101 p., 11 Pls., 3 Figs.

GILLULY, JAMES, AND REESIDE, JOHN B., JR., (1928) *Sedimentary Rocks of the San Rafael Swell and some Adjacent Areas in Eastern Utah,* U. S. Geol. Survey, Prof. Paper 150, p. 61–110

GOODRICH, CALVIN (1944) *Pleuroceridae of the Great Basin,* Univ. Mich., Mus. Zool., Occas. Papers, No. 485, 11 p., 2 Figs.

—— (1945) Goniobasis livescens *of Michigan,* Univ. Mich., Mus. Zool., Misc. Publ., No. 64, 36 p., 1 Pl., 1 Fig., 1 map

GREGORY, HERBERT E. (1950) *Geology of Eastern Iron County, Utah,* Utah Geol. and Mineralogical Survey, Bull. No. 37, 153 p., 53 Pls.

GREGORY, H. E. AND MOORE, RAYMOND C. (1931) *The Kaiparowits Region, a Geographic and Geologic Reconnaissance of Parts of Utah and Arizona,* U. S. Geol. Survey, Prof. Paper 164, 161 p., 31 Pls., 9 Figs.

HALL, JAMES (1845) *Nature of the Geological Formations occupying the Portions of Oregon and North California included in a Geographical Survey under the Direction of Captain Fremont; and Descriptions of Organic Remains collected by Captain J. C. Fremont in the Geographical Survey of Oregon and North California,* in J. C. FREMONT: *A Report of the Exploring Expedition to the Rocky Mountains in the year 1842, and to Oregon and North California in the years 1843–44,* p. 295–310

HENDERSON, JUNIUS (1935) *Fossil Non-Marine Mollusca of North America,* Geol. Soc. Am., Spec. Paper 3, 313 p.

KINDLE, EDWARD M. (1927) *The Rôle of Thermal Stratification in Lacustrine Sedimentation,* Roy. Soc. Canada, Trans., vol. 21, ser. 3, sec. 4, p. 1–35, 3 Pls., 6 Figs.

LA ROCQUE, AURÈLE (1935) *The Molluscan Fauna of Meach Lake, Quebec,* Can. Jour. Res., vol. 13, p. 45–59

—— (1951) *Molluscan Fauna of the Flagstaff Formation, Central Utah,* (Abstract), Geol. Soc. Am., Bull., vol. 62, p. 1457–1458

—— (1952) *Molluscan Faunas of the Orleton Mastodon Site, Madison County, Ohio,* Ohio Jour. Sci., vol. 52, p. 10–27

MEEK, FIELDING B. (1870) *Preliminary Paleontological Report, consisting of Lists of Fossils, with Descriptions of some new Types, etc.,* U. S. Geol. and Geogr. Surv. Territories (Hayden Survey), 4th Ann. Rept., p. 287–318

—— (1872) *Preliminary Paleontological Report, consisting of Lists and Descriptions of*

Fossils, with Remarks on the ages of the Rocks in which they were found, etc., U. S. Geol. and Geogr. Survey Terr. (Hayden Survey), 6th Ann. Rept., p. 431–541

—— (1876) *A Report on the Invertebrate Cretaceous and Tertiary Fossils of the Upper Missouri Country,* U. S. Geol. and Geogr. Survey Terr. (Hayden Survey), vol. 9, 629 p., 45 Pls., 85 Figs.

MEEK, FIELDING B., AND HAYDEN, FERDINAND V. (1856) *Descriptions of New Species of Acephala and Gastropoda from the Tertiary Formations of Nebraska Territory.* Philadelphia, Acad. Natur. Sci., Proc., vol. 8, p. 111–126

—— (1860) *Systematic Catalogue, with Synonymy . . . of Jurassic, Cretaceous and Tertiary Fossils collected in Nebraska . . . under the Command of Lieut. G. K. Warren, of U. S. Topographical Engineers,* Philadelphia, Acad. Nat. Sci., Proc., vol. 12, p. 417–432

PECK, RAYMOND E., AND REKER, CARL C. (1948) *Eocene Charophyta from North America,* Jour. Paleont., vol. 22, p. 85–90, Pl. 21

PILSBRY, HENRY A. (1925) *A Freshwater Snail, Physa zionis, living under unusual Conditions,* Philadelphia, Acad. Nat. Sci., Proc., vol. 77, p. 325–328, Pl. 11

—— (1934) *Mollusks of the Fresh-Water Pliocene Beds of the Kettleman Hills and Neighboring Oil Fields, California,* Philadelphia, Acad. Nat. Sci., Proc., vol. 86, p. 541–570

—— (1939) *Land Mollusca of North America (North of Mexico),* vol. 1, pt. 1, Philadelphia, Acad. Nat. Sci., Monograph 3, 573 p.

—— (1946) *Land Mollusca of North America (North of Mexico),* vol. 2, pt. 1, Philadelphia, Acad. Nat. Sci., Monograph 3, 520 p.

—— (1948) *Land Mollusca of North America (North of Mexico),* vol. 2, pt. 2, Philadelphia, Acad. Nat. Sci., Monograph 3, p. 520–1113.

RUSSELL, LORIS S. (1926) *Mollusca of the Paskapoo Formation in Alberta,* Roy. Soc. Canada, Trans., vol. 20, sec. 4, p. 207–220, 3 Pls.

—— (1931) *Mollusca from the Upper Cretaceous and Lower Tertiary of Alberta,* Roy. Soc. Canada, Trans., vol. 25, sec. 4, p. 9–19, 2 Pls.

—— (1934) *Reclassification of the Fossil Unionidae (Fresh-Water Mussels) of Western Canada,* Canadian Field-Nat., vol. 48, p. 1–4

SCHOFF, STUART L. (1951) *Geology of the Cedar Hills, Utah,* Geol. Soc. Am., Bull., vol. 62, p. 619–646, 2 Pls. 5 Figs.

SEARS, J. D., AND BRADLEY, W. H. (1925) *Relations of the Wasatch and Green River Formations in Northwestern Colorado and Southern Wyoming,* U. S. Geol. Survey, Prof. Paper 132, p. 93–107

SPIEKER, EDMUND M. (1931) *The Wasatch Plateau Coal Field, Utah,* U. S. Geol. Survey, Bull. 819, p. 39–47

—— (1936) *Orogenic History of Central Utah,* Science, vol. 83, p. 62–63

—— (1946) *Late Mesozoic and Early Cenozoic History of Central Utah,* U. S. Geol. Survey, Prof. Paper 205-D, p. 117–161, Pls. 18–25, Figs. 14–21

—— (1949) *The Transition Between the Colorado Plateaus and the Great Basin in Central Utah,* Utah Geol. Soc., Guidebook to the Geology of Utah No. 4, 106 p., map, 10 Figs.

SPIEKER, EDMUND M., AND REESIDE, JOHN B., JR. (1925) *Cretaceous and Tertiary Formations of the Wasatch Plateau, Utah,* Geol. Soc. Am., Bull., vol. 36, p. 435–454

—— (1926) *Upper Cretaceous Shore Line in Utah,* Geol. Soc. Am. Bull., vol. 37, p. 429–438

TRYON, GEORGE W., JR. (1883) *Structural and Systematic Conchology: An Introduction to the Study of the Mollusca,* Phila., publ. by the author, vol. 2, 430 p., Pls. 23–91

WALKER, BRYANT (1918) *A Synopsis of the Classification of the Fresh-Water Mollusca of North America,* Univ. Mich., Mus. Zool., Misc. Publ., No. 6, 88 p.

WHITE, CHARLES A. (1876a) *Report upon the Invertebrate Fossils collected in Portions of Nevada, Utah, Colorado, New Mexico, and Arizona, by Parties of the Expeditions of 1871, 1872, 1873 and 1874,* U. S. Geogr. Survey West of 100th Meridian (Wheeler Survey), vol. 4, pt. 1, 219 p.

—— (1876b) *Invertebrate Paleontology of the Plateau Province,* in POWELL, J. W., *Report on the Geology of the Eastern Portion of the Uinta Mountains . . . ,* U. S. Geol. and Geogr. Survey Terr., p. 74–135

—— (1877) *Paleontological Papers, No. 3. Catalogue of the Invertebrate Fossils Hitherto Published from the Fresh- and Brackish-Water Deposits of the Western Portion of North America,* U. S. Geol. and Geogr. Survey Terr. (Hayden Survey), Bull. 3, p. 607–614

—— (1880a) *On the Antiquity of Certain Subordinate Types of Fresh-Water and Land Mollusca,* Am. Jour. Sci., 3d ser., vol. 20, p. 44–49

—— (1880b) *Descriptions of New Invertebrate Fossils from the Mesozoic and Cenozoic Rocks of Arkansas, Wyoming, Colorado and Utah,* U. S. Nat'l. Mus., Proc., vol. 3, p. 157–162

—— (1883) *A Review of the Non-Marine Fossil Mollusca of North America,* U. S. Geol. Survey, 3d Ann. Rept., p. 403–550, Pls. 1–32

—— (1886) *On the Relation of the Laramie Molluscan Fauna to that of the Succeeding Fresh-Water Eocene and other Groups,* U. S. Geol. Survey, Bull. 34, 54 p.

WHITEAVES, JOSEPH F. (1885) *Report on the Invertebrata of the Laramie and Cretaceous Rocks of the Vicinity of the Bow and Belly Rivers and Adjacent Localities in the North-west Territory,* Canada Geol. Survey, Contr. to Canad. Paleont., vol. 1, part 1, p. 1–89, Pls. 1–11

YEN, TENG-CHIEN (1946) *Paleocene Freshwater Mollusks from Sheridan County, Wyoming,* Am. Jour. Sci., vol. 244, p. 41–48, Pl. 1

—— (1948a) *Eocene Fresh-Water Mollusca from Wyoming,* Jour. Paleont., vol. 22, p. 634–640

—— (1948b) *Paleocene Fresh-Water Mollusks from Southern Montana,* U. S. Geol. Survey, Prof. Paper 214–C, p. 35–50, Pl. 10

—— (1949) *A New Name for* Carinorbis *Yen,* Jour. Paleont., vol. 23, p. 573

EXPLANATION OF PLATES

PLATE 1.—*ELLIPTIO* AND *LAMPSILIS*

Page

Figures

1–8. *Elliptio (Plesielliptio) mendax* (White) 17

1. Umbonal region of a specimen with both valves, showing umbonal sculpture. Hypotype No. 20880, lower part of Flagstaff formation, Locality 36. × 1

2. Umbonal sculpture of another specimen, enlarged to show umbonal ridges and postumbonal striations above the umbonal ridges. Hypotype No. 20879, lower part of Flagstaff formation, Locality 14. × 6

3. Interior of a fragmentary right valve, showing dentition. Hypotype No. 20875, lower part of Flagstaff formation, Locality 3. × 1

4. Interior of an incomplete left valve, showing dentition and muscle scars. Hypotype No. 20874, lower part of Flagstaff formation, Locality 3. × 1

5. Exterior of a crushed left valve, showing ornamentation and extent of the postumbonal ridges. Hypotype No. 20965, lower part of Flagstaff formation, Locality 14. ×1

6. Dorsal view of a specimen with both valves, showing thickness, umbonal sculpture, and posterodorsal ridges. Hypotype No. 20879, lower part of Flagstaff formation, Locality 14. × 0.75

7. Exterior of a left valve, showing the outline and ornamentation of the commoner (female?) form. Hypotype No. 20879, lower part of Flagstaff formation, Locality 14. × 1

8. Exterior of the left valve of a specimen with both valves, showing proportions of the rarer, posteriorly narrowed (male?) form. Hypotype No. 20880, lower part of Flagstaff formation, Locality 36. × 1

9–12. *Elliptio (Elliptio) mormonum* La Rocque, sp. nov. 17

9. Umbonal sculpture of the right valve of the holotype, showing umbonal ridges; compare with Figure 2 of this plate. The same specimen is shown natural size in Fig. 11 of this plate. Holotype No. 20876, upper part of Flagstaff formation, Locality 1. × 3

10. Exterior of the left valve of a fragmentary specimen, showing proportions and ornamentation; note wormlike lines on the shell, exposed by erosion, possibly caused by a parasite. Paratype No. 20882, upper part of Flagstaff formation, Locality 1. × 1

11. Exterior of the right valve of the holotype, showing outline and ornamentation. Holotype No. 20876, upper part of Flagstaff formation, Locality 1. × 1

12. Side view of a specimen with both valves, the largest collected, showing the umbonal sculpture and dentition of the left valve and the beak region of the exfoliated right valve. Paratype No. 20881, upper part of Flagstaff formation, Locality 1. × 1

13–18. *Lampsilis spiekeri* La Rocque, sp. nov. 18

13. Exterior of a small left valve, the holotype, showing outline and ornamentation. Holotype No. 20872, upper part of Flagstaff formation, Locality 1. × 1

14. Interior of the holotype, showing dentition and muscle scars. Holotype No. 20872, upper part of Flagstaff formation, Locality 1. × 1

15. Interior of a right valve, showing outline, dentition, and anterior muscle scar. Paratype No. 20873, upper part of Flagstaff formation, Locality 1. × 1

16. Umbonal sculpture of the same specimen as in Figure 15 of this plate, showing the numerous double-looped ridges. Paratype No. 20873, upper part of Flagstaff formation, Locality 1. × 6

17. Umbonal sculpture of the same specimen as in Figures 15 and 16 of this plate, less enlarged, showing nature of the beak and its relationship to the hinge line. Paratype No. 20873, upper part of Flagstaff formation, Locality 1. × 3

18. Exterior of the left valve of a fragmentary specimen, the largest collected, showing outline and ornamentation; note the large size of the beaks as compared with *Elliptio mendax* and *E. mormonum*. Paratype No. 20883, upper part of Flagstaff formation, Locality 1. × 1

ELLIPTIO AND *LAMPSILIS*

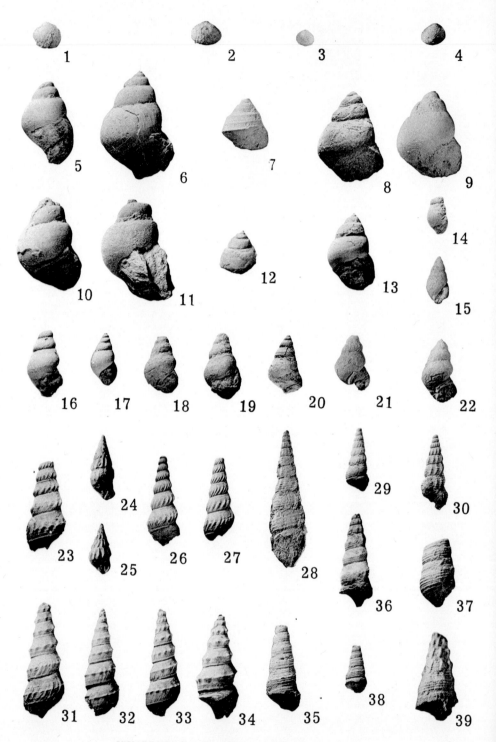

SPHAERIIDAE AND OPERCULATE GASTROPODS

PLATE 2.—SPHAERIIDAE AND OPERCULATE GASTROPODS

Page

Figures

1. Side view of the left valve of a specimen with both valves, showing outline and position of the beaks. Hypotype No. 20860, lower part of Flagstaff formation, Locality 20. × 1
2. Side view of the right valve of a smaller specimen, showing outline. Hypotype No. 20929, lower part of Flagstaff formation, Locality 20. × 3

3. Exterior of a right valve, showing outline of the shell and position of the beaks. Hypotype No. 20927, lower part of Flagstaff formation, Locality 20. × 3
4. Exterior of a right valve, showing outline of a slightly larger specimen. Hypotype No. 20928, lower part of Flagstaff formation, Locality 20. × 3

5. An incomplete specimen with faint angulations on the early whorls only, showing one extreme of variation in the development of spiral ornamentation. Hypotype No. 20861, lower part of Flagstaff formation, Locality 13. × 1
6. An adult specimen, the largest collected, showing the axial ornamentation, the upper part of the aperture, and the umbilical chink. Hypotype No. 20864, lower part of Flagstaff formation, Locality 13. × 1
7. A young specimen, showing extreme development of spiral cords. Hypotype No. 20870, lower part of Flagstaff formation, Locality 12. × 1
8. An adult specimen, showing strongly angulated early whorls and rounded body whorl; the parietal callus entirely closes the umbilicus; compare with Figure 6 of this plate. Hypotype No. 20865, lower part of Flagstaff formation, Locality 20. × 1
9. A specimen from the same bed as Figure 7 of this plate, showing weak development of spiral cords which are barely visible angulations on the first three whorls and entirely absent on the fourth and fifth. Hypotype No. 20871, lower part of Flagstaff formation, Locality 12. × 1

10. A large, uncrushed specimen from which most of the shell has been exfoliated, showing the proportions of the whorls. Hypotype No. 20866, upper part of Flagstaff formation, Locality 38. × 1.
11. Internal mold of the largest specimen collected, showing proportions of the whorls. Hypotype No. 20867, upper part of Flagstaff formation, Locality 40. × 1
12. A small, crushed specimen, showing the axial ornamentation. Hypotype No. 20884, upper part of Flagstaff formation, Locality 1. × 1
13. A specimen of medium size, exfoliated except for the earlier whorls, showing character of the spire. Hypotype No. 20885, upper part of Flagstaff formation, Locality 2. × 1

14. An incomplete specimen, showing the body whorl and well-preserved aperture. Hypotype No. 20863, lower part of Flagstaff formation, Locality 20. × 1
15. An almost complete specimen, the largest collected, showing the narrow, uninflated whorls. Compare with *L. mariana*, Figures 16–18 of this plate. Hypotype No. 20887, lower part of Flagstaff formation, Locality 20. × 1

16. A large specimen with the test preserved, showing slightly angulated early whorls and part of the aperture. Hypotype No. 20877, lower part of Flagstaff formation, Locality 12. × 1
17. A smaller but complete specimen, showing apical whorls and aperture. Compare with *L. limnaeiformis*, Figures 14 and 15 of this plate. Hypotype No. 20878, lower part of Flagstaff formation, Locality 8. × 1
18. An incomplete, weathered specimen, showing part of the aperture and the reflection

of the parietal wall over the umbilicus. Hypotype No. 20886, lower part of Flagstaff formation, Locality 20. × 1

19–22. *Lioplacodes tenuicarinata* (Meek and Hayden) 26

19. A well-preserved specimen, the largest collected, showing subdued spiral ornamentation. Hypotype No. 20868, lower part of Flagstaff formation, Locality 20. × 1

20. A specimen of average size, showing well-developed spiral ornamentation. Hypotype No. 20869, lower part of Flagstaff formation, Locality 20. × 1

21. A weathered specimen of average size, showing the upper part of the aperture and the reflection of the parietal wall over the umbilicus, which is reduced to a small chink. Hypotype No. 20862, lower part of Flagstaff formation, Locality 20. × 1

22. A specimen with well-preserved aperture, showing a slightly decollated last whorl. Hypotype No. 20859, lower part of Flagstaff formation, Locality 20. × 1

23–27. *Goniobasis tenera* (Hall), form A 29

23. An incomplete specimen, the largest collected, showing persistence of axial and spiral ornamentation in the later whorls and restriction of axial plications to the central part of the whorl. Hypotype No. 20888, lower part of Flagstaff formation, Locality 30. × 1

24. A young specimen, magnified, showing character of ornamentation on the early whorls. Hypotype No. 20890, lower part of Flagstaff formation, Locality 10. × 3

25. A still smaller specimen than Figure 24 of this plate, showing the character of the ornamentation on the early whorls. Hypotype No. 20891, lower part of Flagstaff formation, Locality 10. × 3

26. A well-preserved specimen of average size, showing the ornamentation, especially the basal spiral cords and the persistent axial plications. Hypotype No. 20905, lower part of Flagstaff formation, Locality 31. × 1

27. A smaller specimen than Figure 26 of this plate, showing ornamentation. Hypotype No. 20889, lower part of Flagstaff formation, Locality 9. × 1

28–30. *Goniobasis tenera* (Hall), form B 30

28. An almost complete specimen, the largest collected, showing persistent spiral carinae on all whorls and reduced axial plications on the later whorls. Hypotype No. 20892, upper part of Flagstaff formation, Locality 2. × 1

29. An immature specimen with worn apical whorls, showing well-preserved ornamentation on later whorls. Hypotype No. 20894, upper part of Flagstaff formation, Locality 2. × 1

30. An immature specimen with well-preserved ornamentation, showing carinae and plications, the latter not developed into nodes. Hypotype No. 20893, upper part of Flagstaff formation, Locality 2. × 1

31–34. *Goniobasis tenera* (Hall), form C 30

31. A specimen lacking the apical whorls, showing development of form C pattern in middle whorls and reversion to form A pattern in later whorls. Hypotype No. 20897, Colton formation, Locality 54. × 1

32. A specimen with almost complete spire, showing typical development of form C pattern. Hypotype No. 20895, Colton formation, Locality 54. × 1

33. A specimen lacking the apical whorls, showing extreme reduction of axial ornamentation in the later whorls. Hypotype No. 20898, Colton formation, Locality 54. × 1

34. A specimen with almost complete apex, showing early, strong development of axial plications into strong nodes. Hypotype No. 20899, Colton formation, Locality 54. × 1

35–39. *Goniobasis tenera* (Hall), form D 30

35. An incomplete specimen, showing absence of axial ornamentation on the middle whorls of the shell. Hypotype No. 20903, lower part of Flagstaff formation, Locality 20. × 1

36. Another incomplete specimen showing incomplete attenuation of the axial ornamentation which is still present but not as strong as the spiral carinae. Hypotype No. 20904, lower part of Flagstaff formation, Locality 20. × 1

37. A large, incomplete specimen, showing absence of axial plications on last two whorls. Hypotype No. 20902, lower part of Flagstaff formation, Locality 20. × 1

38. An incomplete specimen showing early whorls with strong spiral and without axial ornamentation. Hypotype No. 20901, lower part of Flagstaff formation, Locality 20. × 1
39. A small specimen, magnified, showing strong axial and spiral ornamentation on the first four whorls and spiral ornamentation only on the next two. Hypotype No. 20900, lower part of Flagstaff formation, Locality 20. × 4

PLATE 3.—*HYDROBIA, MICROPYRGUS, PLEUROLIMNAEA, GYRAULUS, CARINULORBIS,* AND *PHYSA*

Figures   Page

1–4. *Hydrobia utahensis* White   31
1. An almost complete specimen of the wide (female?) form, showing the flattened early whorls and slightly inflated body whorl. Hypotype No. 20930, lower part of Flagstaff formation, Locality 47. × 3
2. Another specimen of the wide (female?) form, showing faint angulation at the base of the body whorl. Hypotype No. 20931, lower part of Flagstaff formation, Locality 41. × 3
3. A specimen of the narrow (male?) form, showing outline. Hypotype No. 20932, lower part of Flagstaff formation, Locality 16. × 3
4. Another specimen of the narrow (male?) form showing faint axial striae. Hypotype No. 20933, lower part of Flagstaff formation, Locality 34. × 3

5–7. *Hydrobia* cf. *H. recta* White   32
5. An average adult specimen, showing typically irregular growth after the sixth whorl. Hypotype No. 20935, lower part of Flagstaff formation, Locality 24. × 3
6. A specimen of only six whorls, showing regular growth to that point; specimens of this size are very similar to the narrow form of *H. utahensis* White but slightly narrower. Hypotype No. 20936, lower part of Flagstaff formation, Locality 31. × 3
7. A specimen of 5.5 whorls, showing the nature of the apical whorls. Hypotype No. 20095, lower part of Flagstaff formation, Locality 34. × 3

8–9. *Hydrobia ephraimensis* La Rocque, sp. nov.   33
8. An almost complete but somewhat exfoliated specimen, the largest collected, showing well-impressed sutures and rounded whorls. The aperture is buried in the matrix. Holotype No. 20937, upper part of Flagstaff formation, Locality 29. × 3
9. A smaller specimen, unexfoliated, showing character of the apical whorls. Paratype No. 20938, upper part of Flagstaff formation, Locality 29. × 3

10–13. *Micropyrgus minutulus* (Meek and Hayden)   34
10. A specimen with the aperture lacking, one of the largest collected, showing the elongate spire and the basal angulation of the whorls. Hypotype No. 20943, lower part of Flagstaff formation, Locality 20. × 3
11. Another large specimen with poorly preserved aperture, showing a more regularly developed shell. Hypotype No. 20944, lower part of Flagstaff formation, Locality 20. × 3
12. A small specimen with irregular growth, showing basal angulation of whorls and character of the aperture. Hypotype No. 20945, lower part of Flagstaff formation, Locality 20. × 3
13. A large specimen with incomplete aperture, showing irregular growth. Compare with Fig. 10 of this plate. Hypotype No. 20946, lower part of Flagstaff formation, Locality 20. × 3

14–16. *Pleurolimnaea tenuicosta* (Meek and Hayden)   35
14. An almost complete specimen with poorly preserved surface, showing general outline of the shell and aperture. Hypotype No. 20948, lower part of Flagstaff formation, Locality 16. × 2.5
15. A specimen lacking the basal part of the aperture, showing the pointed spire, axial striae, and the character of the upper part of the aperture. Hypotype No. 20947, lower part of Flagstaff formation, Locality 20. × 2.5
16. An incomplete specimen showing the character of the aperture, especially the parietal margin and the axial striae. Hypotype No. 20045, lower part of Flagstaff formation, Locality 25. × 3

17–18. *Gyraulus militaris* (White) 37
17. Apical view of a small specimen, much enlarged, showing the general aspect of the shell. Hypotype No. 20951, lower part of Flagstaff formation, Locality 16. × 6
18. Umbilical view of a specimen, less enlarged than Figure 19 of this plate, showing deep and wide umbilicus. Hypotype No. 20950, lower part of Flagstaff formation, Locality 17. × 3

19–22. *Gyraulus aequalis* (White) 37
19. Umbilical view of a small specimen, an internal mold, showing deep, narrow umbilicus. Hypotype No. 20057, upper part of Flagstaff formation, Locality 29. × 3
20. Umbilical view of another internal mold, slightly weathered, showing character of the inner whorls. Hypotype No. 20952, upper part of Flagstaff formation, Locality 29. × 3
21. Apical view of a specimen with exfoliated body whorl, showing the slightly sunken spire. Hypotype No. 20953, upper part of Flagstaff formation, Locality 29. × 3
22. Apical view of a slightly crushed specimen with exfoliated body whorl, showing slightly sunken spire. Hypotype No. 20954, upper part of Flagstaff formation, Locality 29. × 2.5

23–26. *Carinulorbis utahensis* La Rocque, sp. nov. 38
23. Side view of a small specimen, showing carinae and rounded periphery. Holotype, No. 20955, lower part of Flagstaff formation, Locality 46. × 3
24. Apical (?) view of the same specimen, showing position of upper (?) carina and apical (?) whorls. Holotype No. 20955, lower part of Flagstaff formation, Locality 46. × 3
25. Side view of another specimen, showing cross section of the whorl. Paratype No. 20956, lower part of Flagstaff formation, Locality 46. × 3
26. Apical (?) view of the same specimen, showing sharp upper (?) carina and depressed spire (?). Paratype No. 20956, lower part of Flagstaff formation, Locality 46. × 3

27–29. *Physa bridgerensis* Meek 40
27. Side view of a large, well-preserved specimen, showing proportions of the long-spired form. Hypotype No. 20064, lower part of Flagstaff formation, Locality 5. × 1
28. Side view of an internal mold of a large specimen, showing proportions of the short-spired form. The spire seems even shorter than it is, as the first few apical whorls are lacking. Hypotype No. 20906, lower part of Flagstaff formation, Locality 9. × 1
29. A fragmentary specimen intermediate between the long and short forms, showing surface ornamentation of fine axial striae. Hypotype No. 20092, lower part of Flagstaff formation, Locality 9. × 1

30–32. *Physa pleromatis* White 40
30. A crushed specimen, the largest collected in the upper part of the Flagstaff, showing the globose shell. The apex has been crushed inward but can still be seen. Hypotype No. 20908, upper part of Flagstaff formation, Locality 29. × 1
31. An internal mold of average size in the Flagstaff formation, showing the short form of the species. The dark area in the upper left-hand part of the figure is a natural break in the matrix. Hypotype No. 20909, upper part of the Flagstaff formation, Locality 38. × 1
32. Another internal mold, with well-preserved spire, showing the high-spired form of the species. Hypotype No. 20907, upper part of Flagstaff formation, Locality 1. × 1

33–35. *Physa* cf. *P. longiuscula* Meek and Hayden 41
33. An internal mold, the largest collected, with some of the shell still preserved, showing the robust spire of this species. Hypotype No. 20912, upper part of Flagstaff formation, Locality 2. × 1
34. Side view of another internal mold, showing the usual size of Flagstaff specimens. Hypotype No. 20910, upper part of Flagstaff formation, Locality 2. × 1
35. An uncrushed internal mold, showing the relationship of the spire to the aperture. Hypotype No. 20911, upper part of Flagstaff formation, Locality 2. × 1

36–38. *Physa* cf. *P. rhomboidea* Meek and Hayden 41

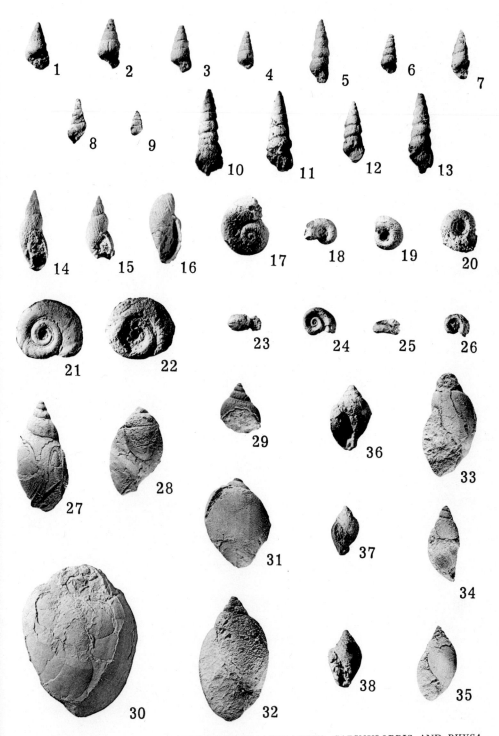

HYDROBIA, MICROPYRGUS, PLEUROLIMNAEA, GYRAULUS, CARINULORBIS, AND PHYSA

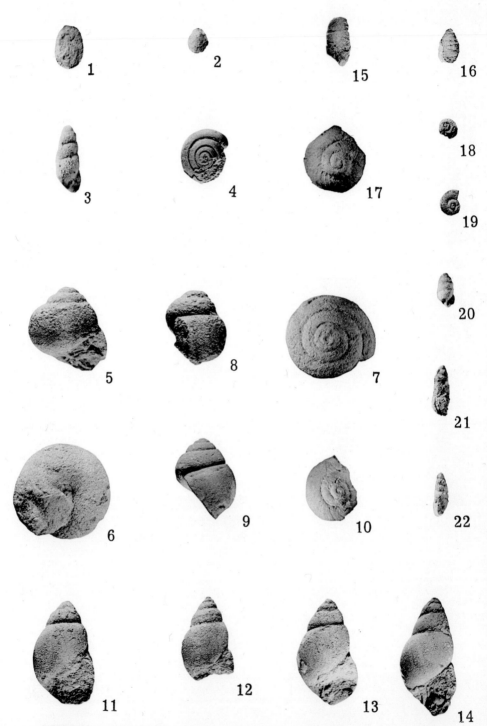

FERRISSIA, CARYCHIUM, "HELIX," OREOHELIX, BULIMULUS?, HOLOSPIRA, DISCUS, GASTROCOPTA?, AND ALBERTANELLA

36. An immature specimen, enlarged, showing character of the spire and aperture. Hypotype No. 20913, lower part of Flagstaff formation, Locality 9. × 3
37. An immature specimen, enlarged, showing a narrower form of the species. Hypotype No. 20915, lower part of Flagstaff formation, Locality 9. × 3
38. An immature specimen, somewhat crushed, showing some of the axial striae. Hypotype No. 20914, lower part of Flagstaff formation, Locality 9. × 3

PLATE 4.—*FERRISSIA, CARYCHIUM, "HELIX," OREOHELIX, BULIMULUS?, HOLOSPIRA, DISCUS, GASTROCOPTA?,* AND *ALBERTANELLA*

Figures   Page

1–2. *Ferrissia actinophora* (White) 43
1. A fragmentary, partly exfoliated specimen, the largest collected, showing the outline of the mature shell. Hypotype No. 20957, upper part of Flagstaff formation, Locality 29. × 3
2. A smaller but better preserved specimen. showing outline and position of the apex. Hypotype No. 20958, upper part of Flagstaff formation, Locality 29. × 3

3. *Carychium* cf. *C. exile* H. C. Lea 44
3. Side view of one of the best specimens collected, showing character of apex, whorls, and aperture. Hypotype No. 20896, lower part of Flagstaff formation, Locality 20. × 6

4–9. *"Helix" riparia* White 45
4. Apical view of a small, imperfect internal mold, showing regularly enlarging whorls. Hypotype No. 20916, upper part of Flagstaff formation, Locality 40. × 1
5. Side view of a large internal mold, showing globose shell and upper part of the aperture. A small patch of original shell on the left of the last whorl shows faint axial striae. Hypotype No. 20917, middle part of Flagstaff formation, Locality 44. × 1
6. Umbilical view of an internal mold, the largest collected, showing large size of the species and possible reflection of the lip over the umbilicus. Hypotype No. 20918, middle or upper part of Flagstaff formation, Locality 48. × 1
7. Apical view of a large internal mold, the same specimen as in Figure 5 of this plate, showing the gradual regular increase of the whorls. Hypotype No. 20917, middle part of Flagstaff formation, Locality 44. × 1
8. Side view of an internal mold, showing probable inclination of the aperture. Hypotype No. 20919, middle or upper part of Flagstaff formation, Locality 51. × 1
9. Side view of an internal mold of a relatively high-spired form, showing downbending of the last whorl and probable inclination of the aperture. Hypotype No. 20920, middle or upper part of Flagstaff formation, Locality 6. × 1

10. *Oreohelix* sp. 47
10. Apical view of a well-preserved specimen, showing large apical whorls and the axial striae. Hypotype No. 20962, lower part of Flagstaff formation, Locality 42. × 1

11–14. *Bulimulus?* sp. 48
11. Side view of the internal mold of a globose specimen, showing character of the whorls and aperture. Hypotype No. 20922, middle or upper part of Flagstaff formation, Locality 48. × 1
12. Side view of a more elongate specimen, showing traces of growth lines. Hypotype No. 20921, middle or upper part of Flagstaff formation, Locality 48. × 1
13. A large, globose internal mold, showing the lower part of the aperture. Hypotype No. 20923, middle or upper part of Flagstaff formation, Locality 50. × 1
14. An elongate internal mold, the largest collected, showing the character of the adult or nearly adult shell and probable reflection of the parietal wall over the umbilicus. Hypotype No. 20924, middle or upper part of Flagstaff formation, Locality 50. × 1

15–16. *Holospira* cf. *H. leidyi* (Meek) 49
15. A fragmentary internal mold, showing the cylindrical aspect of the shell. Hypotype No. 20925, middle or upper part of Flagstaff formation, Locality 51. × 1
16. A poorly preserved specimen showing the distinctive aspect of the whorls even in fragmentary specimens. Hypotype No. 20926, middle or upper part of Flagstaff formation, Locality 49. × 1

17–19. *Discus* cf. *D. ralstonensis* (Cockerell) 50

17. A well-preserved specimen, enlarged, showing character of apical whorls and axial striae. Hypotype No. 20961, lower part of Flagstaff formation, Locality 35. × 3

18. A small specimen of only two whorls, partly exfoliated, showing the character of most Flagstaff specimens of this species. Hypotype No. 20960, lower part of Flagstaff formation, Locality 28. × 3

19. A somewhat larger exfoliated specimen of 2½ whorls, showing the character of the whorls. Hypotype No. 20959, lower part of Flagstaff formation, Locality 28. × 3

20. *Gastrocopta?* sp. 50

20. Side view of a well-preserved specimen, showing the blunt apex, open umbilicus, and aperture. Hypotype No. 20052, lower part of Flagstaff formation, Locality 27. × 3

21–22. *Albertanella minuta* Russell 51

21. A small, well-preserved specimen, greatly enlarged, showing the sinistral spire and narrow aperture. Hypotype No. 20964, lower part of Flagstaff formation, Locality 24. × 6

22. A small specimen, greatly enlarged, showing the character of the apical whorls. Hypotype No. 20963, lower part of Flagstaff formation, Locality 24. × 6

INDEX